The Expanding Role of

Mass Spectrometry

in

Biotechnology

Second Edition

The Expanding Role of Mass Spectrometry in Biotechnology

Second Edition

Gary Siuzdak

The Scripps Research Institute

MCC Press
San Diego

"All you have to decide is what to do with the time that is given to you."

- anonymous, from a 14th century manuscript "Clouds of Consciousness" as translated by Monika Hasserodt

Preface

My first book "Mass Spectrometry for Biotechnology" introduced the capabilities of mass spectrometry and improvements during the period between 1985 and 1994. These developments continued and were largely covered in the 2003 first edition of The Expanding Role of Mass Spectrometry in Biotechnology. This 2nd edition includes further improvements to the graphics and descriptions as well as covering new advances in mass spectrometry technology.

Acknowledgments

I express my sincere gratitude to my friends and colleagues (following page) who helped review and edit this manuscript, especially Liz Want and Michael Greig for their contributions to chapters 8 and 9. The editing imprint of Jennifer Bardi can be found on almost every page of the first three chapters and I also thank Darlene Custodio for her extraordinary effort in putting this book together from cover to cover.

I am also grateful to Richard Lerner who has created an environment at Scripps that fosters interdisciplinary research, in which the development and application of mass spectrometry thrive.

Darlene Custodio

Jennifer O'Sullivan

Elizabeth Want

Chuan Qin

Junefredo V Apon

Sunia Trauger

Bill Webb

Theodore Brandon

Ben Bolaños

Thomas Hollenbeck

Andrew Meyers

Grace O'Maille

Bruce Jon Compton

Ken Harris

Melissa Zolodz

Richard Kriwacki

Eric Peters

Stu Borman

Martin Sonderegger

Michael Greig

Sebastian Wendeborn

Table of Contents

A Mass Spectrometry History

"I felt at that moment that it was my chance to do one thing supremely well." - *Roger Bannister*

Mass spectrometry has a special intrigue that comes from its interdisciplinary nature, as it freely crosses the borders of physics, chemistry and biology. Its history goes back to the early 1900's, and its development has reached a pinnacle in recent years (1-21). Hundreds of women and men have contributed to the development of MS, and this timeline highlights some key individuals and events in the history of the field (http://masspec.scripps.edu).

Early Mass Spectrometry – The Physical Roots

The history of MS begins with Sir J.J. Thomson (3-5) (**Figure 1**) of the University of Cambridge. Thomson's "theoretical and experimental investigations on the conduction of electricity by gases" led to the discovery of the electron in 1897, for which he was awarded the 1906 Nobel Prize in Physics. In the first decade of the 20th century Thomson went on to construct the first mass spectrometer (then called a parabola spectrograph), in which ions were separated by their different parabolic trajectories in electromagnetic fields and detection occurred when the ions struck a fluorescent screen or photographic plate.

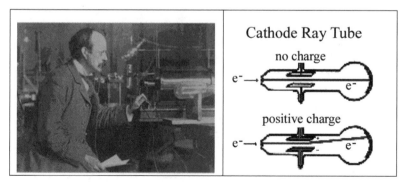

Figure 1. J.J. Thomson (1906 Nobel Prize in Physics) and a cathode ray tube used to perform some of the first m/z measurements. Deflection of electrons was observed when the electric field was turned on.

Later, Thomson's protégé, Francis W. Aston (1922 Nobel Prize in Chemistry, **Figure 2**) of the University of Cambridge, designed a mass spectrometer that improved MS resolving power, allowing Aston to study isotopes (6-8). During this same period, A. J. Dempster of the University of Chicago also improved upon resolution (9) with a magnetic analyzer and developed the first electron ionization source, which ionized volatilized molecules with a beam of electrons. Electron ionization ion sources are still very widely used in modern mass spectrometers for small molecule analysis. Thomson, Aston, and Dempster created a strong foundation of MS theory and instrument design that made it possible for those who followed to develop instruments capable of meeting the demands of chemists and biologists.

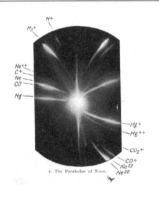

Figure 2. Aston photograph made by the positive rays after they underwent electric and magnetic deflections, resulting in isotope separation.

Francis William Aston
1922 Nobel Prize in Chemistry

Improving the Mass Analyzer: Branching into Chemical and Biological Applications

An important goal, particularly for chemists, was to create an instrument capable of analyzing both the elements and small organic molecules. The answer to this problem eventually came in four different forms: magnetic sector double-focusing, time-of-flight, quadrupole, and Fourier transform ion cyclotron resonance mass analyzers. In its time, the most widely used high mass-resolution double-focusing instrument was developed by Professor Alfred O. C. Nier (10) at the University of Minnesota during World War II to perform isotopic analysis and separate uranium-235 from uranium-238. The first nuclear bomb was developed entirely from the uranium separated by this type of mass spectrometer (11).

The concept of time-of-flight mass spectrometry (TOF MS) was proposed in 1946 by William E. Stephens (12) of the University of Pennsylvania. In a TOF analyzer, ions are separated by differences in their velocities as they move in a straight path toward a collector. TOF MS allows for rapid analyses (<100 milliseconds), it is capable of high resolving power and high accuracy, it is applicable to rapid chromatographic detection, and it is now used for the mass determination of large biomolecules because of its virtually limitless mass range.

One type of mass analyzer that proved to be ideal for coupling to gas chromatography and, more recently, liquid chromatography was the quadrupole mass filter, first reported in the mid-1950s by Wolfgang Paul (13) (**Figure 3**) of the University of Bonn, who shared the 1989 Nobel Prize in Physics for his work on ion trapping. In a quadrupole device, a quadrupolar electrical field (comprising radiofrequency and direct-current components) is used to separate ions.

quadrupole

ion trap

Figure 3. Paul's development of the quadrupole and quadrupole ion trap resulted in two of the most used mass analyzers.	Wolfgang Paul 1989 Nobel Prize in Physics

Although quadrupole mass spectrometers are not as accurate and precise as double-focusing instruments, they offer excellent dynamic range, are quite stable, and are also readily applied to tandem mass spectrometry experiments – features that make them popular for quantitative analysis and drug discovery applications.

Ion cyclotron resonance MS (ICR MS) has proved to be the ultimate MS solution for high resolution and high accuracy. ICR was initially described by John A. Hipple (14) of the National Bureau of Standards, Washington, D.C. It operates by subjecting ions to a simultaneous radiofrequency electric field and a uniform magnetic field, causing the ions to follow spiral paths in an analyzer chamber. By scanning the radiofrequency or magnetic field, the ions can be detected sequentially. In 1974, Melvin B. Comisarow and Alan G. Marshall of the University of British Columbia revolutionized ICR by developing Fourier transform ICR mass spectrometry (15) **(Figure 4)** (FTMS). The major advantage of FTMS is that it allows many different ions to be measured at once. Sub-part per million accuracy – such as an error of less than 0.001 Dalton for a 1000 Dalton peptide – is now routinely possible with commercial FTMS instruments.

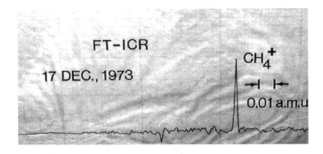

Figure 4. First FTMS mass spectrum, courtesy of Alan Marshall.

All of these mass analyzer designs, and combinations of different techniques for tandem mass spectrometry, are widely used today and are continually being developed for new applications.

Improvements in Ionization: Blossoming into Biology

Despite advances in mass accuracy, mass range, quantitative analysis, and the ability to couple the instruments to chromatography, MS still lacked efficacy for large and small biomolecule analysis. Significant molecular decomposition or fragmentation during vaporization/ionization and poor sensitivity proved very problematic in biomolecular MS. The development of "soft ionization" – electrospray ionization MS (ESI MS) and matrix-assisted laser desorption/ionization MS (MALDI MS) – allowed MS to transcend into the realm of biology (**Figure 5**).

In ESI MS, highly charged droplets dispersed from a capillary in an electric field are evaporated, and the resulting ions are drawn into an MS inlet. The technique was first conceived in the 1960s by chemistry professor Malcolm Dole (16) of Northwestern University but not put into practice for biomolecule analysis until the early 1980s by John B. Fenn (17) of Yale University.

Figure 5. Electrospray ionization (ESI) and matrix-assisted laser desorption/ionization (MALDI) mass spectrometry have revolutionized protein and drug analysis.

In matrix-assisted laser desorption/ionization (MALDI) MS, analyte molecules are laser-desorbed from a solid or liquid UV-absorbing matrix. The technique was initially reported by Koichi Tanaka (18) and coworkers at Shimadzu Corp., Kyoto, Japan, and was also developed by Franz Hillenkamp and Michael Karas (19) at the University of Frankfurt, Germany.

For their work on developing soft ionization techniques suitable for large biomolecule analysis, Fenn and Tanaka shared in the 2002 Nobel Prize in Chemistry. Their work on ESI-MS and MALDI-MS made MS increasingly useful for sophisticated biological experiments. Applications include: protein identification, drug discovery, DNA sequencing, carbohydrate analysis, and biomarker discovery.

Small Molecule Analysis and Protein Characterization: Maturation

The importance of these developments can be seen in research efforts at every major pharmaceutical company and university in the world today. Arguably the two most important MS applications are pharmacokinetics for small molecule drug analysis and protein identification (20) using "peptide mass mapping" (**Figure 6**). Recently, the analysis of small endogenous biomolecules by mass spectrometry has also found its way into clinical studies, and it is being widely used in rapid and inexpensive neonatal screens for over 30 different diseases (2).

Protein Characterization

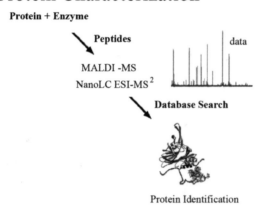

Protein + Enzyme

Peptides

MALDI -MS

NanoLC ESI-MS ^{2}

data

Database Search

Protein Identification

MS/MS for drug discovery

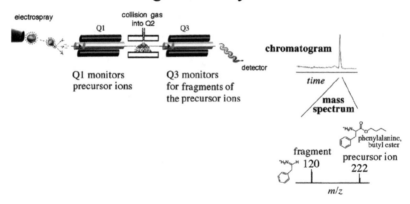

electrospray

collision gas into Q2

Q1

Q3

detector

Q1 monitors precursor ions

Q3 monitors for fragments of the precursor ions

chromatogram

time

mass spectrum

fragment 120

precursor ion 222

phenylalanine, butyl ester

m/z

Figure 6. MALDI and nanoliquid chromatography ESI tandem MS strategies are now routinely used for protein identification, and ESI tandem mass spectrometry is very valuable in the quantitation of small biomolecules for drug discovery and for disease diagnosis in neonatal screening.

The Limits of Biological Mass Spectrometry: Toward Whole Organism Analysis

Soft ionization MS methods have made it possible to study increasingly larger structures. Bruce Ganem and Jack Henion of Cornell University and Brian Chait at Rockefeller University have clearly demonstrated the utility of such methods for analyzing noncovalent interactions (21-23), and Carol Robinson (24) of Cambridge University has even examined subcellular components. Novel ESI instrumentation designed by Henry Benner at Lawrence Berkeley Laboratory (25) has made it possible to measure intact viral ions measuring millions of Daltons (25-27), and such experiments have shown that mass-analyzed viruses maintain their structure and virulence (**Figure 7**).

Intact Viral Analysis

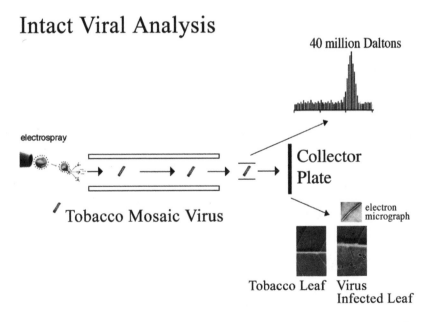

Figure 7. Study demonstrating whole virus analysis by mass spectroemetry and viability of virus following mass analysis (25-27).

Historical Developments in Mass Spectrometry

Investigator(s)	Year	Contribution
J.J. Thomson	1899-1911	First Mass Spectrometer
Dempster	1918	Electron Ionization and Magnetic Focusing
Aston	1919	Atomic Weights using MS
Mattauch & Herzog	1934	Double Focusing Instruments
Stephens	1946	Time-of-Flight Mass Analysis
Hipple, Sommer & Thomas	1949	Ion Cyclotron Resonance
Johnson & Nier	1953	Reverse Geometry Double Focusing Instruments
Paul & Steinwedel	1953	Quadrupole Analyzers
Beynon	1956	High Resolution MS
McLafferty and Ryahe	1959-1963	GC/MS
Biemann, Cone, Webster, & Arsenault	1966	Peptide sequencing
Munson & Field	1966	Chemical Ionization
Dole	1968	Electrospray Ionization
Beckey	1969	Field Desorption-MS of Organic Molecules
MacFarlane & Torgerson	1974	Plasma Desorption-MS
Comisarow & Marshall	1974	FT ICR MS
Yost & Enke	1978	Triple Quadrupole MS
Barber	1981	Fast Atom Bombardment (FAB)
Fenn	1984	ESI on Biomolecules
Tanaka, Karas, & Hillenkamp	1985-8	Matrix facilitated laser desorption/ionization

Investigator(s)	Year	Contribution
Fenn	1984	ESI on Biomolecules
Chowdhury, Katta & Chait	1990	Protein Conformational Changes with ESI-MS
Ganem, Li, & Henion Chait & Katta	1991	Noncovalent Complexes with ESI-MS
Pieles, Zurcher, Schär, & Moser	1993	Oligonucleotide ladder Sequencing
Henzel, Billeci, Stults, Wong, Grimley, & Watanabe	1993	Protein Mass Mapping
Benner, Siuzdak, Bothner, & Fuerstenau	1996-2001	Intact Viral Analysis

Useful References

This article is based in part on an earlier article in Today's Chemist by Stu Borman (Chemical & Engineering News, Washington, DC) and Hailey Russell and Gary Siuzdak (The Center for Mass Spectrometry, The Scripps Research Institute, La Jolla, CA).

Thomson JJ. *On the Masses of the Ions in Gases at Low Pressures*. Philosophical Magazine. **1899**, 48:295, 547-567.

Thomson JJ. *On Rays of Positive Electricity*. The London, Edinburgh, and Dublin Philosophical Magazine and Journal of Science. **1907**, XLVII.

Thomson JJ. *Rays of Positive Electricity*. Phil. Mag. **1911**, 6:20, 752-67.

Dempster AJ. *A new method of positive ray analysis*. Phys. Rev. **1918**, 11, 316-24.

Aston FW. *A Positive Ray Spectrograph (Plate IX)*. London, Edinburgh and Dublin Philosophical Magazine and Journal of Science. **1919**, 6:38:228, 709.

Aston FW. *Isotopes and Atomic Weights*. Nature. **1920**, 105, 617.

Aston FW. *The Mass-Spectra of Chemical Elements*. Phil. Mag. **1920**, 39, 611-25.

Stephens W. Phys. Rev. **1946**, 69, 691

Hipple JA, Sommer H, Thomas HA. *A Precise Method of Determining the Faraday by Magnetic Resonance*. Phys. Rev. **1949**, 76, 1877-1878.

Nier AO. *A double-focusing mass spectrometer*. Natl. Bur. Standards(U.S.) Circ. **1953**, 522, 29-36.

Paul W, Steinwedel H. *A new mass spectrometer without magnetic field*. Z. Naturforsch. **1953**, 8A, 448-450.

Dole M, Mack LL, Hines RL, Mobley RC, Ferguson LD, Alice MB. *Molecular beams of macroions*. Journal of Chemical Physics. **1968**, 49:5, 2240-2249.

Comisarow MB, Marshall AG. *Fourier transform ion cyclotron resonance [FT-ICR] spectroscopy.* Chem. Phys. Lett. **1974**, 25:2, 282-283.

Tanaka K, Waki H, Ido Y, Akita S, Yoshida Y., Yoshida T. *Protein and polymer analysis up to m/z 100,000 by laser ionization time-of-flight mass spectrometry.* Rapid Commun. Mass Spectrom. **1988**, 2, 151.

Karas M, Hillenkamp F. *Laser desorption ionization of proteins with molecular mass exceeding 10,000 Daltons.* Anal. Chem. **1988**, 60, 2299-2301.

Fenn JB, Mann M, Meng CK, Wong SF, Whitehouse CM. *Electrospray Ionization for Mass Spectrometry of Large Biomolecules.* Science. **1989**, 246, 64-71.

Ganem B, Li YT, Henion JD. *Detection of Noncovalent Receptor Ligand Complexes by Mass Spectrometry.* Journal of the American Chemical Society. **1991**, 113:16, 6294-6296.

Katta V, Chait BT. *Conformational Changes In Proteins Probed By Hydrogen-Exchange Electrospray-Ionization Mass Spectrometry.* Rapid Communications In Mass Spectrometry. **1991**, V5:N4, 214-217.

Katta V, Chait BT. *Observation Of The Heme Globin Complex In Native Myoglobin By Electrospray-Ionization Mass Spectrometry.* Journal Of The American Chemical Society. **1991**, V113:N22, 8534-8535.

Henzel WJ, Billeci TM, Stults JT, Wong SC, Grimley C, Watanabe C. *Identifying Proteins From 2-Dimensional Gels By Molecular Mass Searching of Peptide Fragments in Protein Sequence Databases.* Proceedings Of The National Academy Of Sciences Of The United States Of America. **1993**, V90:N11, 5011-5015.

Siuzdak G, Bothner B, Yeager M, Brugidou C, Fauquet CM, Hoey K., Chang C.M. *Mass Spectrometry and Viral Analysis.* Chemistry & Biology. **1996**, 3, 45.

Yergey AL, Yergey AK. *Preparative Scale Mass Spectrometry: A Brief History of the Calutron.* JASMS. **1997**, V8:N9, 943-953.

Rostom AA, Fucini P, Benjamin DR, Juenemann R, Nierhaus KH, Hartl FU, Dobson CM, Robinson CV. *Detection and Characterization of Intact Ribosomes in the Gas Phase of a Mass Spectrometer.* Proc. Natl. Acad. Sci. USA. **2000**, 10, 5185-5190.

Fuerstenau SD, Benner WH, Thomas JJ, Brugidou C, Bothner B, Siuzdak G. *Mass Spectrometry of an Intact Virus.* Angewandte Chemie. **2001**, 40, 542-544.

Chace, DH. *Mass Spectrometry in the Clinical Laboratory.* Chem. Rev. **2001**, 101, 445-477.

Thomas JJ, Bothner B, Traina J, Benner WH, Siuzdak G. *Electrospray Ion Mobility Spectrometry of Intact Viruses.* Spectroscopy, in press.

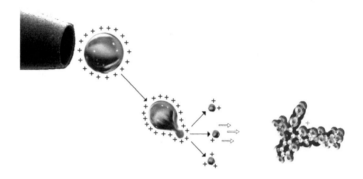

Chapter 1
Ionization and the Mass Spectrometer

"Whatever you can do, or think you can do, begin it. Boldness has power, and genius, and magic in it." – Goethe

Perspective

Mass spectrometry has been described as the smallest scale in the world, not because of the mass spectrometer's size but because of the size of what it weighs -- molecules. Over the past decade, mass spectrometry has undergone tremendous technological improvements allowing for its application to proteins, peptides, carbohydrates, DNA, drugs, and many other biologically relevant molecules. Due to ionization sources such as electrospray ionization and matrix-assisted laser desorption/ ionization (MALDI), mass spectrometry has become an irreplaceable tool in the biological sciences. This chapter provides an overview of mass spectrometry, focusing on ionization sources and their significance in the development of mass spectrometry in biomolecular analysis.

A mass spectrometer determines the mass of a molecule by measuring the mass-to-charge ratio (m/z) of its ion. Ions are generated by inducing either the loss or gain of a charge from a neutral species. Once formed, ions are electrostatically directed into a mass analyzer where they are separated according to m/z and finally detected. The result of molecular ionization, ion separation, and ion detection is a spectrum that can provide molecular mass and even structural information. An analogy can be drawn between a mass spectrometer and a prism, as shown in **Figure 1.1**. In the prism, light is separated into its component wavelengths which are then detected with an optical receptor, such as visualization. Similarly, in a mass spectrometer the generated ions are separated in the mass analyzer, digitized and detected by an ion detector (such as an electron multiplier, Chapter 2).

Mass Spectrometry Prism Analogy

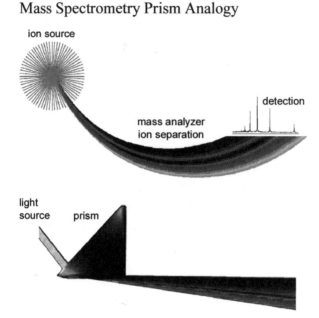

Figure 1.1. The mass analysis process as compared to the dispersion of light by a prism.

What is Mass Spectrometry?

John B. Fenn, the originator of electrospray ionization for biomolecules and the 2002 Nobel Laureate in Chemistry, probably gave the most apt answer to this question:

> *Mass spectrometry is the art of measuring atoms and molecules to determine their molecular weight. Such mass or weight information is sometimes sufficient, frequently necessary, and always useful in determining the identity of a species. To practice this art one puts charge on the molecules of interest, i.e., the analyte, then measures how the trajectories of the resulting ions respond in vacuum to various combinations of electric and magnetic fields.*

Clearly, the sine qua non of such a method is the conversion of neutral analyte molecules into ions. For small and simple species the ionization is readily carried by gas-phase encounters between the neutral molecules and electrons, photons, or other ions. In recent years, the efforts of many investigators have led to new techniques for producing ions of species too large and complex to be vaporized without substantial, even catastrophic, decomposition.

Some Basics

Four basic components are, for the most part, standard in all mass spectrometers (**Figure 1.2**): a sample inlet, an ionization source, a mass analyzer and an ion detector. Some instruments combine the sample inlet and the ionization source, while others combine the mass analyzer and the detector. However, all sample molecules undergo the same processes regardless of instrument configuration. Sample molecules are introduced into the instrument through a sample inlet. Once inside the instrument, the sample molecules are converted to ions in the ionization source, before being electrostatically propelled into the mass analyzer. Ions are then separated according to their m/z within the mass analyzer. The detector converts the ion energy into electrical signals, which are then transmitted to a computer.

Sample Introduction Techniques

Sample introduction was an early challenge in mass spectrometry. In order to perform mass analysis on a sample, which is initially at atmospheric pressure (760 torr), it must be introduced into the instrument in such a way that the vacuum inside the instrument remains relatively unchanged ($\sim10^{-6}$ torr). The most common methods of sample introduction are direct insertion with a probe or plate commonly used with MALDI-MS, direct infusion or injection into the ionization source such as ESI-MS.

Mass Spectrometer Components

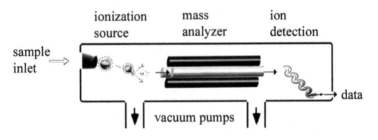

Figure 1.2. Components of a mass spectrometer. Note that the ion source does not have to be within the vacuum of the mass spectrometer. For instance, ESI and APCI are at atmospheric pressure and are known as atmospheric pressure ionization (API) sources.

Direct Insertion: Using an insertion probe/plate (**Figure 1.3**) is a very simple way to introduce a sample into an instrument. The sample is first placed onto a probe and then inserted into the ionization region of the mass spectrometer, typically through a vacuum interlock. The sample is then subjected to any number of desorption processes, such as laser desorption or direct heating, to facilitate vaporization and ionization.

Direct Infusion: A simple capillary or a capillary column is used to introduce a sample as a gas or in solution. Direct infusion is also useful because it can efficiently introduce small quantities of sample into a mass spectrometer without compromising the vacuum. Capillary columns are routinely used to interface separation techniques with the ionization source of a mass spectrometer. These techniques, including gas chromatography (GC) and liquid chromatography (LC), also serve to separate a solution's different components prior to mass analysis. In gas chromatography, separation of different components occurs within a glass capillary column. As the vaporized sample exits the gas chromatograph, it is directly introduced into the mass spectrometer.

In the 1980s the incapability of liquid chromatography (LC) with mass spectrometry was due largely to the ionization techniques being unable to handle the continuous flow of LC. However, electrospray ionization (ESI), atmospheric pressure chemical ionization (APCI) and atmospheric pressure photoionization (APPI) now allows LC/MS to be performed routinely (**Figure 1.4**).

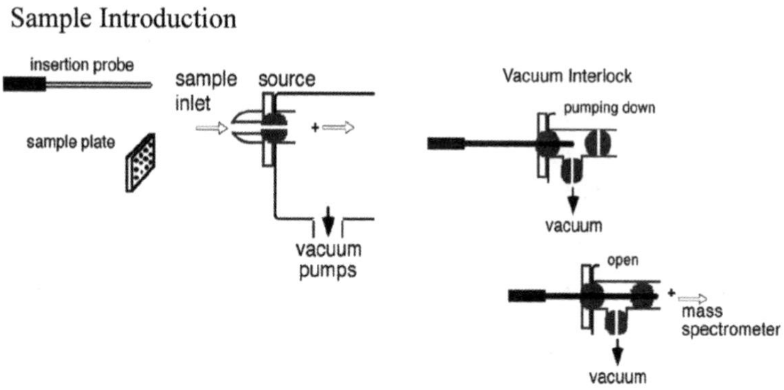

Sample Introduction

Figure 1.3. Samples are often introduced into the mass spectrometer using a direct insertion probe, a capillary column (EI with GC/MS or ESI) or a sample plate (MALDI). The vacuum interlock allows for the vacuum of the mass spectrometer to be maintained while the instrument is not in use. It also allows for the sample (at atmospheric pressure) to be introduced into the high vacuum of the mass spectrometer.

Liquid Chromatography Mass Spectrometry

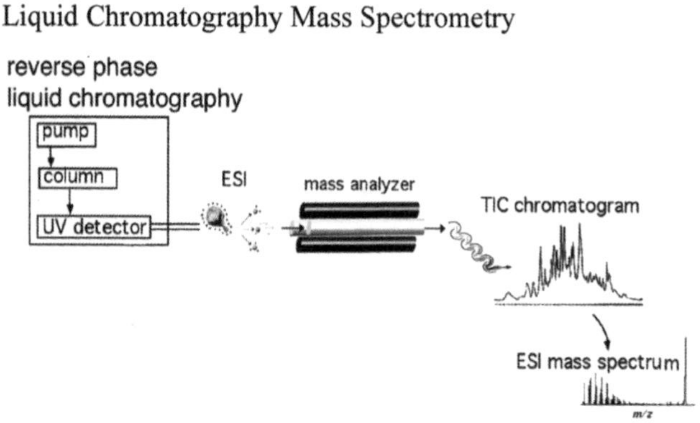

Figure 1.4. Interfacing liquid chromatography with electrospray ionization mass spectrometry. Liquid chromatography/mass spectrometry (LC/MS) ion chromatogram and the corresponding electrospray mass spectrum are shown. Gas chromatography mass spectrometry (GC/MS) produces results in much the same way as LC/MS, however, GC/MS uses an electron ionization source, which is limited by thermal vaporization (UV refers to ultraviolet and TIC is the total ion current).

Ionization

Ionization method refers to the mechanism of ionization while the ionization source is the mechanical device that allows ionization to occur. The different ionization methods, summarized here, work by either ionizing a neutral molecule through electron ejection, electron capture, protonation, cationization, or deprotonation, or by transferring a charged molecule from a condensed phase to the gas phase.

Protonation

Scheme 1.1. An example of a mass spectrum obtained via protonation.

$$M + H^+ \rightarrow MH^+$$
$$H_2N\text{-RGASRR-OH} + H^+ \rightarrow MH^+$$

peptide

relative int. (%)

$[M+2H]^{2+}$

MH^+
702.4

50   750

m/z

Protonation is a method of ionization by which a proton is added to a molecule, producing a net positive charge of 1+ for every proton added. Positive charges tend to reside on the more basic residues of the molecule, such as amines, to form stable cations. Peptides are often ionized via protonation. Protonation can be achieved via matrix-assisted laser desorption/-ionization (MALDI), electrospray ionization (ESI) and atmospheric pressure chemical ionization (APCI).

Deprotonation

Scheme 1.2. An example of a mass spectrum of sialic acid obtained via deprotonation.

$$M - H^+ \rightarrow [M-H]^-$$

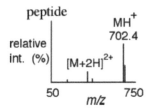

sialic acid

relative int. (%)

$[M-H]^-$
308.1

10   330

m/z

Deprotonation is an ionization method by which the net negative charge of 1- is achieved through the removal of a proton from a molecule. This mechanism of ionization, commonly achieved via MALDI, ESI, and APCI is very useful for acidic species including phenols, carboxylic acids, and sulfonic acids. The negative ion mass spectrum of sialic acid is shown in **Scheme 1.2**.

Cationization

Scheme 1.3. An example of a mass spectrum obtained via cationization.

M + Cation⁺ → MCation⁺

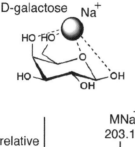

D-galactose

relative int. (%)

MNa⁺ 203.1

Cationization is a method of ionization that produces a charged complex by non-covalently adding a positively charged ion to a neutral molecule. While protonation could fall under this same definition, cationization is distinct for its addition of a cation adduct other than a proton (e.g. alkali, ammonium). Moreover, it is known to be useful with molecules unstable to protonation. The binding of cations other than protons to a molecule is naturally less covalent, therefore, the charge remains localized on the cation. This minimizes delocalization of the charge and fragmentation of the molecule. Cationization is commonly achieved via MALDI, ESI, and APCI. Carbohydrates are excellent candidates for this ionization mechanism, with Na+ a common cation adduct.

Transfer of a charged molecule to the gas phase

Scheme 1.4. An example of a mass spectrum of tetraphenylphosphine obtained via transfer of a charged species from solution into the gas phase.

M⁺ solution → M⁺ gas

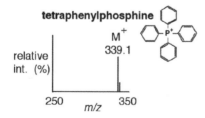

tetraphenylphosphine

relative int. (%)

M⁺ 339.1

The transfer of compounds already charged in solution is normally achieved through the desorption or ejection of the charged species from the condensed phase into the gas phase. This transfer is commonly achieved via MALDI or ESI. The positive ion mass spectrum of tetraphenylphosphine is shown in **Scheme 1.4.**

Electron ejection

Scheme 1.5. An example of a mass spectrum obtained via electron ejection.

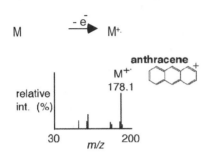

As its name implies, **electron ejection** achieves ionization through the ejection of an electron to produce a 1$^+$ net positive charge, often forming radical cations. Observed most commonly with electron ionization (EI) sources, electron ejection is usually performed on relatively nonpolar compounds with low molecular weights and it is also known to generate significant fragment ions. The mass spectrum resulting from electron ejection of anthracene is shown in **Scheme 1.5**.

Electron capture

Scheme 1.6. An example of a mass spectrum obtained via electron capture. Electron capture is commonly achieved via electron ionization (EI).

M $\xrightarrow{+\ \bar{e}}$ M$^-$

hexachlorobenzene

relative int. (%)

M^{--}
283.8

230   290
m/z

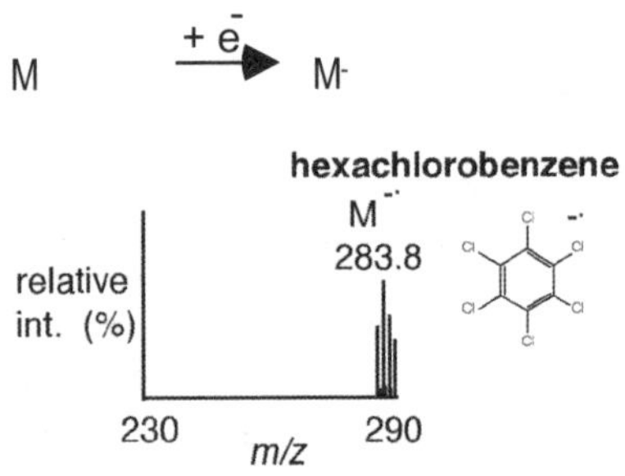

With the **electron capture** ionization method, a net negative charge of 1- is achieved with the absorption or capture of an electron. It is a mechanism of ionization primarily observed for molecules with a high electron affinity, such as halogenated compounds. The electron capture mass spectrum of hexachlorobenzene is shown in **Scheme 1.6**.

Table 1.1. Ionization methods, advantages and disadvantages.

Ionization Method	Advantages	Disadvantages
Protonation (positive ions)	— many compounds will accept a proton to become ionized — many ionization sources such as ESI, APCI, FAB, CI and MALDI will generate these species	— some compounds are not stable to protonation (i.e. carbohydrates) or cannot accept a proton easily (i.e. hydrocarbons)
Cationization (positive ions)	— many compounds will accept a cation, such as Na$^+$ or K$^+$ to become ionized — many ionization sources such as ESI, APCI, FAB and MALDI will generate these species	— tandem mass spectrometry experiments on cationized molecules will often generate limited or no fragmentation information
Deprotonation (negative ions)	— most useful for compounds that are somewhat acidic — many ionization sources such as ESI, APCI, FAB, CI and MALDI will generate these species	— compound specific
Transfer of charged molecule to gas phase (positive or negative ions)	— useful when the compound is already charged — many ionization sources such as ESI, APCI, FAB and MALDI will generate these species	— only useful for precharged ions
Electron ejection (positive ions)	— observed with electron ionization and can provide molecular mass as well as fragmentation information	— often generates too much fragmentation — it can be unclear whether the highest mass ion is the molecular ion or a fragment
Electron capture (negative ions)	— observed with electron ionization and can provide molecular mass as well as fragmentation information	— often generates too much fragmentation — it can be unclear whether the highest mass ion is the molecular ion or a fragment

Ionization Sources

Prior to the 1980s, electron ionization (EI) was the primary ionization source for mass analysis. However, EI limited chemists and biochemists to small molecules well below the mass range of common bio-organic compounds. This limitation motivated scientists such as John B. Fenn, Koichi Tanaka, Franz Hillenkamp, Michael Karas, Graham Cooks, and Michael Barber to develop the new generation of ionization techniques, including fast atom/ion bombardment (FAB), matrix-assisted laser desorption/ionization (MALDI), and electrospray ionization (ESI) (Table 1.2). These techniques have revolutionized biomolecular analyses, especially for large molecules. Among them, ESI and MALDI have clearly evolved to be the methods of choice when it comes to biomolecular analysis.

Table 1.2

Ionization Source	Acronym	Event
Electrospray ionization	ESI	evaporation of charged droplets
Nanoelectrospray ionization	nanoESI	evaporation of charged droplets
Atmospheric pressure chemical ionization	APCI	corona discharge and proton transfer
Matrix-assisted laser desorption/ionization	MALDI	photon absorption/proton transfer
Desorption/ionization on silicon	DIOS	photon absorption/proton transfer
Fast atom/ion bombardment	FAB	ion desorption/proton transfer
Electron ionization	EI	electron beam/electron transfer
Chemical ionization	CI	proton transfer

MALDI and ESI are now the most common ionization sources for biomolecular mass spectrometry, offering excellent mass range and sensitivity (**Figure 1.5**). The following section will focus on the principles of ionization sources, providing some details on the practical aspects of their use as well as ionization mechanisms.

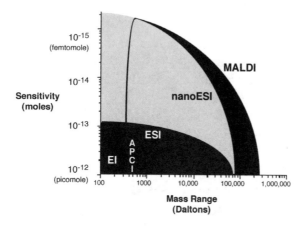

Figure 1.5. A glance at the typical sensitivity and mass ranges allowed by different ionization techniques provides a clear answer to the question of which are most useful; electron ionization (EI), atmospheric pressure chemical ionization (APCI) and desorption/ionization on silicon (DIOS) are somewhat limiting in terms of upper mass range, while electrospray ionization (ESI), nanoelectrospray ionization (nanoESI), and matrix-assisted laser desorption ionization (MALDI) have a high practical mass range.

Electrospray Ionization

The idea of electrospray, while not new, has been rejuvenated with its recent application to biomolecules. The first electrospray experiments were carried out by Chapman in the late 1930s and the practical development of electrospray ionization for mass spectrometry was accomplished by Dole in the late 1960s. Dole also discovered the important phenomenon of multiple charging of molecules. It was Fenn's work that ultimately led to the modern day technique of electrospray ionization mass spectrometry and its application to biological macromolecules.

A more physical explanation of ESI is that the needle voltage produces an electrical gradient on the fluid which separates the charges at the surface. This forces the liquid to emerge from the needle as a Taylor cone. The tip of the Taylor cone protrudes as a filament until the liquid reaches the Rayleigh limit where the surface tension and electrostatic repulsion are equal and the highly charged droplets leave the filament. The droplets that break away from the filament are attracted to the entrance of the mass spectrometer due to the high opposite voltage at the mass analyzer's entrance. As the droplet moves towards the analyzers, the Coulombic repulsion on the surface exceeds the surface tension, the droplet explodes into smaller droplets ultimately releasing ions.

Electrospray Ionization

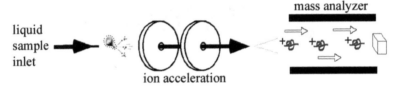

Figure 1.6. Electrospray ionization (ESI) mass spectrometry.

Electrospray ionization (ESI) is a method routinely used with peptides, proteins, carbohydrates, small oligonucleotides, synthetic polymers, and lipids. ESI produces gaseous ionized molecules directly from a liquid solution. It operates by creating a fine spray of highly charged droplets in the presence of an electric field. (An illustration of the electrospray ionization process is shown in **Figures 1.6** and **1.7**). The sample solution is sprayed from a region of the strong electric field at the tip of a metal nozzle maintained at a potential of anywhere from 700 V to 5000 V. The nozzle (or needle) to which the potential is applied serves to disperse the solution into a fine spray of charged droplets. Either dry gas, heat, or both are applied to the droplets at atmospheric pressure thus causing the solvent to evaporate from each droplet. As the size of the charged droplet decreases, the charge density on its surface increases. The mutual Coulombic repulsion between like charges on this surface becomes so great that it exceeds the forces of surface tension, and ions are ejected from the droplet through a "Taylor cone" **Figure 1.7**. Another possibility is that the droplet explodes releasing the ions. In either case, the emerging ions are directed into an orifice through electrostatic lenses leading to the vacuum of the mass analyzer. Because ESI involves the continuous introduction of solution, it is suitable for using as an interface with HPLC or capillary electrophoresis.

Positive and Negative ESI

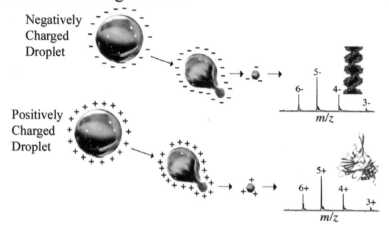

Negatively Charged Droplet

Positively Charged Droplet

Figure 1.7. Positive and negative ESI of an oligonucleotide (top) and a protein (bottom).

Electrospray ionization is conducive to the formation of singly charged small molecules, but is also well-known for producing multiply charged species of larger molecules. This is an important phenomenon because the mass spectrometer measures the mass-to-charge ratio (m/z) and therefore multiple charging makes it possible to observe very large molecules with an instrument having a relatively small mass range. Fortunately, the software available with all electrospray mass spectrometers facilitates the molecular weight calculations necessary to determine the actual mass of the multiply-charged species. **Figures 1.8** and **1.9** illustrate the different charge states on two different proteins, where each of the peaks in the mass spectra can be associated with different charge states of the molecular ion. Multiple charging has other important advantages in tandem mass spectrometry. One advantage is that upon fragmentation you observe more fragment ions with multiply charged precursor ions than with singly charged precursor ions.

Multiple charging: A 10,000 Da protein and its theoretical mass spectrum with up to five charges are shown in **Figure 1.8**. The mass of the protein remains the same, yet the m/z ratio varies depending upon the number of charges on the protein. Protein ionization is usually the result of protonation, which not only adds charge but also increases the mass of the protein by the number of protons added. This effect on the m/z applies equally for any mechanism of molecular ionization resulting in a positively or negatively charged molecular ion, including the addition or ejection of charge-carrying species other than protons (e.g. Na^+ and Cs^+). Multiple positive charges are observed for proteins, while for oligonucleotides negative charging (with ESI) is typical.

Although electrospray mass spectrometers are equipped with software that will calculate molecular weight, an understanding of how the computer makes such calculations from multiply-charged ions is beneficial. Equations 1.1 - 1.5 and **Figure 1.9** offer a simple explanation, where we assume p1 and p2 are adjacent peaks and differ by a single charge, which is equivalent to the addition of a single proton.

ESI Multiple Charging of a Protein

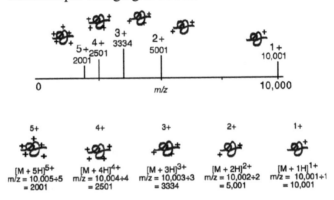

Figure 1.8. A theoretical protein with a molecular weight of 10,000 generates three different peaks with the ions containing 5, 4, and 3 charges, respectively. The mass spectrometer detects each of the protein ions at 2001, 2501, and 3334, respectively.

14

ESI-MS data from Myoglobin

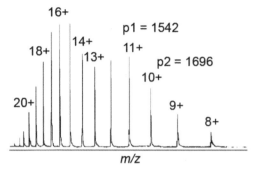

Figure 1.9. The multiply charged ions of myoglobin generated from ESI. The different peaks represent different charge states of myoglobin. The molecular weight can be determined using Equations 1.1 - 1.3.

$p = m/z$	(1.1)
$p1 = (Mr + z1)/z1$	(1.2)
$p2 = \{Mr + (z1 - 1)\}/(z1 - 1)$	(1.3)

p is a peak in the mass spectrum   p1 is the m/z value for p1
m is the total mass of an ion   p2 is the m/z value for p2
z is the total charge   z1 is the charge on peak p1
Mr is the average mass of protein

Equations 1.2 and 1.3 can be solved for the two unknowns, Mr and z1.
For the peaks in the mass spectrum of myoglobin shown in **Figure 1.9**, p1=1542, and p2=1696.

$1542\ z1 = Mr + z1$	(1.4)
$1696\ (z1 - 1) = Mr + (z1 - 1)$	(1.5)

Solving the two equations: Mr = 16,951 Da for z1 = 11

Electrospray Solvents

Many solvents can be used in ESI and are chosen based on the solubility of the compound of interest, the volatility of the solvent and the solvent's ability to donate a proton. Typically, protic primary solvents such as methanol, 50/50 methanol/water, or 50/50 acetonitrile/H_2O are used, while aprotic cosolvents, such as 10% DMSO in water, as well as isopropyl alcohol are used to improve solubility for some compounds. Although 100% water is used in ESI, water's relatively low vapor pressure has a detrimental effect on sensitivity;

better sensitivity is obtained when a volatile organic solvent is added. Some compounds require the use of straight chloroform with 0.1% formic acid added to facilitate ionization. This approach, while less sensitive, can be effective for otherwise insoluble compounds. Buffers such as Na^+, K^+, phosphate, and salts present a problem for ESI by lowering the vapor pressure of the droplets resulting in reduced signal through an increase in droplet surface tension resulting in a reduction of volatility (see Chapter 3 for quantitative information on salt effects). Consequently, volatile buffers such as ammonium acetate can be used more effectively.

Table 1.3. Advantages and disadvantages of electrospray ionization (ESI).

Advantages	Disadvantages
— practical mass range of up to 70,000 Da	— the presence of salts and ion-pairing agents like TFA can reduce sensitivity
— good sensitivity with femtomole to low picomole sensitivity typical	— complex mixtures can reduce sensitivity
— softest ionization method, capable of generating noncovalent complexes in the gas phase	— simultaneous mixture analysis can be poor
— easily adaptable to liquid chromatography	— multiple charging can be confusing especially in mixture analysis
— easily adaptable to tandem mass analyzers such as ion traps and triple quadrupole instruments	— sample purity is important
— multiple charging allows for analysis of high mass ions with a relatively low m/z range instrument	— carryover from sample to sample
— no matrix interference	

Configuration of the Electrospray Ion Source

The off-axis ESI configuration now used in many instruments to introduce the ions into the analyzers (as shown in **Figure 1.10**) has turned out to be very valuable for high flow rate applications. The primary advantage of this configuration is that the flow rates can be increased without contaminating or clogging the inlet. Off-axis spraying is important because the entrance to the analyzer is no longer being saturated by solvent, thus keeping droplets from entering and contaminating the inlet. Instead, only ions are directed toward the inlet. This makes ESI even more compatible with LC/MS at the milliliter per minute flow rates.

Figure 1.10. An example of off-axis ESI.

Nanoelectrospray Ionization (NanoESI)

Low flow electrospray, originally described by Wilm and Mann, has been called nanoelectrospray, nanospray, and micro-electrospray. This ionization source is a variation on ESI, where the spray needle has been made very small and is positioned close to the entrance to the mass analyzer (**Figure 1.11**). The end result of this rather simple adjustment is increased efficiency, which includes a reduction in the amount of sample needed.

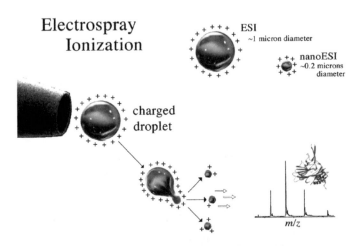

Figure 1.11. Ion formation from electrospray ionization source. The electrospray ionization source uses a stream of air or nitrogen, heat, a vacuum, or a solvent sheath (often methanol) to facilitate desolvation of the droplets. Ejection of the ion occurs through a "Taylor cone" (central droplet) where they are then electrostatically directed into the mass analyzer.

The flow rates for nanoESI sources are on the order of tens to hundreds of nanoliters per minute. In order to obtain these low flow rates, nanoESI uses emitters of pulled and in some cases metallized glass or fused silica that have a small orifice (~5μ). The dissolved sample is added to the emitter and a pressure of ~30 PSI is applied to the back of the emitter. Effusing the sample at very low flow rates allows for high sensitivity. Also, the emitters are positioned very close to the entrance of the mass analyzer, therefore ion transmission to the mass analyzer is much more efficient. For instance, the analysis of a 5 mM solution of a peptide by nanoESI would be performed in 1 minute, consuming ~50 femtomoles of sample. The same experiment performed with normal ESI in the same time period would require 5 picomoles, or 100 times more sample than for nanoESI. In addition, since the droplets are typically smaller with nanoESI than normal ESI (**Figure 1.11**), the amount of evaporation necessary to obtain ion formation is much less. As a consequence, nanoESI is more tolerant of salts and other impurities because less evaporation means the impurities are not concentrated down as much as they are in ESI.

Atmospheric Pressure Chemical Ionization

APCI has also become an important ionization source because it generates ions directly from solution and it is capable of analyzing relatively nonpolar compounds. Similar to electrospray, the liquid effluent of APCI (**Figure 1.12**) is introduced directly into the ionization source. However, the similarity stops there. The droplets are not charged and the APCI source contains a heated vaporizer, which facilitates rapid desolvation/vaporization of the droplets. Vaporized sample molecules are carried through an ion-molecule reaction region at atmospheric pressure.

Atmospheric Pressure Chemical Ionization

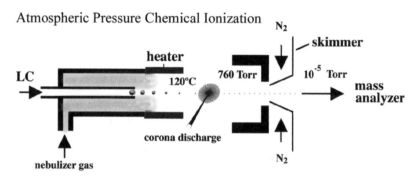

Figure 1.12. Atmospheric pressure chemical ionization (APCI) mass spectrometry.

APCI ionization originates from the solvent being excited/ionized from the corona discharge. Because the solvent ions are present at atmospheric pressure conditions, chemical ionization of analyte molecules is very efficient; at atmospheric pressure analyte molecules collide with the reagent ions frequently. Proton transfer (for protonation MH^+ reactions) occurs in the positive mode, and either electron transfer or proton loss, ($[M-H]^-$) in the negative mode. The moderating influence of the solvent clusters on the reagent ions, and of the high gas pressure, reduces fragmentation during ionization and results in primarily intact molecular ions. Multiple charging is typically not observed presumably because the ionization process is more energetic than ESI.

Atmospheric Pressure Photoionization

Atmospheric pressure photoionization (APPI) has recently become an important ionization source because it generates ions directly from solution with relatively low background and is capable of analyzing relatively nonpolar compounds. Similar to APCI, the liquid effluent of APPI (**Figure 1.13**) is introduced directly into the ionization source. The primary difference between APCI and APPI is that the APPI vaporized sample passes through ultra-violet light (a typical krypton light source emits at 10.0 eV and 10.6 eV). Often, APPI is much more sensitive than ESI or APCI and has been shown to have higher signal-to-noise ratios because of lower background ionization. Lower background signal is largely due to high ionization potential of standard solvents such as methanol and water (IP 10.85 and 12.62 eV, respectively) which are not ionized by the krypton lamp.

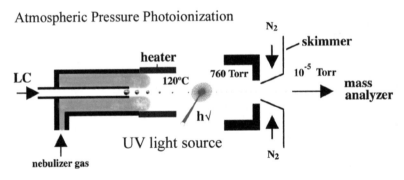

Figure 1.13. Atmospheric pressure photoionization (APPI) mass spectrometry.

A disadvantage of both ESI and APCI is that they can generate background ions from solvents. Additionally, ESI is especially susceptible to ion suppression effects, and APCI requires vaporization temperatures ranging from 350-500° C, which can cause thermal degradation.

APPI induces ionization via two different mechanisms. The first is direct photoexcitation, allowing for electron ejection and the generation of the positive ion radical cation (M^+). The APPI source imparts light energy that is higher than the ionization potentials (IPs) of most target molecules, but lower than most of the IPs of air and solvent molecules, thus removing them as interferants. In addition, because little excess energy is deposited in the molecules, there is minimal fragmentation.

The second mechanism is atmospheric pressure photo-induced chemical ionization which is similar to APCI in that it involves charge transfer to produce protonation (MH^+) or proton loss ($[M-H]^-$) to generate negative ions.

To initiate chemical ionization, a photoionizable reagent, also called a dopant, is added to the eluant. Upon photoionization of the dopant, charge transfer occurs to the analyte. Typical dopants in positive mode include acetone and toluene. Acetone also serves as a dopant in negative mode.

The ionization mechanism (M^+ versus $[M+H]^+$) that a molecule undergoes depends on the proton affinity of the analyte, the solvent, and the type of dopant used.

Matrix-Assisted Laser Desorption/Ionization (MALDI)

Matrix-assisted laser desorption/ionization mass spectrometry (MALDI-MS) was first introduced in 1988 by Tanaka, Karas, and Hillenkamp. It has since become a widespread analytical tool for peptides, proteins, and most other biomolecules (oligonucleotides, carbohydrates, natural products, and lipids). The efficient and directed energy transfer during a matrix-assisted laser-induced desorption event provides high ion yields of the intact analyte, and allows for the measurement of compounds with sub-picomole sensitivity. In addition, the utility of MALDI for the analysis of heterogeneous samples makes it very attractive for the mass analysis of complex biological samples such as proteolytic digests.

Matrix-Assisted Laser Desorption/ Ionization

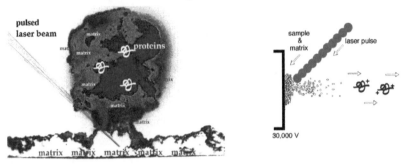

Figure 1.14. The efficient and directed energy transfer of the UV laser pulse during a MALDI event allows for relatively small quantities of sample (femtomole to picomole) to be analyzed. In addition, the utility of MALDI mass spectrometry for the analysis of heterogeneous samples makes it very attractive for the mass analysis of biological samples.

While the exact desorption/ionization mechanism for MALDI is not known, it is generally believed that MALDI causes the ionization and transfer of a sample from the condensed phase to the gas phase via laser excitation and abalation of the sample matrix (**Figure 1.14**). In MALDI analysis, the analyte is first co-crystallized with a large molar excess of a matrix compound, usually a UV-absorbing weak organic acid. Irradiation of this analyte-matrix mixture by a laser results in the vaporization of the matrix, which carries the analyte with it. The matrix plays a key role in this technique. The co-crystallized sample molecules also vaporize, but without having to directly absorb energy from the laser. Molecules sensitive to the laser light are therefore protected from direct UV laser excitation.

> *MALDI matrix -- A nonvolatile solid material facilitates the desorption and ionization process by absorbing the laser radiation. As a result, both the matrix and any sample embedded in the matrix are vaporized. The matrix also serves to minimize sample damage from laser radiation by absorbing most of the incident energy.*

Once in the gas phase, the desorbed charged molecules are then directed electrostatically from the MALDI ionization source into the mass analyzer. Time-of-flight (TOF) mass analyzers are often used to separate the ions according to their mass-to-charge ratio (m/z). The pulsed nature of MALDI is directly applicable to TOF analyzers since the ion's initial time-of-flight can be started with each pulse of the laser and completed when the ion reaches the detector.

Several theories have been developed to explain desorption by MALDI. The thermal-spike model proposes that the ejection of intact molecules is attributed to poor vibrational coupling between the matrix and analyte, which minimizes vibrational energy transfer from the matrix to the vibrational modes of the analyte molecule, thereby minimizing fragmentation. The pressure pulse theory proposes that a pressure gradient from the matrix is created normal to the surface and desorption of large molecules is enhanced by momentum transfer from collisions with these fast moving matrix molecules. It is generally thought that ionization occurs through proton transfer or cationization during the desorption process.

The utility of MALDI for biomolecule analyses lies in its ability to provide molecular weight information on intact molecules. The ability to generate accurate information can be extremely useful for protein identification and characterization. For example, a protein can often be unambiguously identified by the accurate mass analysis of its constituent peptides (produced by either chemical or enzymatic treatment of the sample).

Table 1.4. Advantages and disadvantages of Matrix-Assisted Laser Desorption/Ionization (MALDI).

Advantages	Disadvantages
— practical mass range of up to 300,000 Da. Species of much greater mass have been observed using a high current detector;	— matrix background, which can be a problem for compounds below a mass of 700 Da. This background interference is highly dependent on the matrix material;
— typical sensitivity on the order of low femtomole to low picomole. Attomole sensitivity is possible;	— possibility of photo-degradation by laser desorption/ionization;
— soft ionization with little to no fragmentation observed;	— acidic matrix used in MALDI may cause degradation on some compounds.
— tolerance of salts in millimolar concentrations;	
— suitable for the analysis of complex mixtures.	

Common MALDI matricies

α-cyano-4-hydroxycinnamic acid	3,5-dimethoxy-4-hydroxycinnamic acid	2,5-dihydroxy benzoic acid
(α-cyano or HCCA)	(sinapinic acid)	(DHB)
peptides and glycopeptides	peptides and proteins	peptides and small proteins

MALDI solid matrix contains microcrystals of the matrix with the sample embedded in the crystals.

Figure 1.15. Commonly used MALDI matrices and a MALDI plate showing the matrix deposition. One of the advantages of MALDI is that multiple samples can be prepared at the same time, as seen with this multisample plate.

Sample-matrix preparation procedures greatly influence the quality of MALDI mass spectra of peptides/proteins (**Figure 1.15**). Among the variety of reported preparation methods, the dried-droplet method is the most frequently used. In this case, a saturated matrix solution is mixed with the analyte solution, giving a matrix-to-sample ratio of about 5000:1. An aliquot (0.5-2.0 μL) of this mixture is then applied to the sample target where it is allowed to dry. Below is an example of how the dried-droplet method is performed:

— Pipet 0.5 μL of sample to the sample plate.

— Pipet 0.5 μL of matrix to the sample plate.

— Mix the sample and matrix by drawing the combined droplet in and out of the pipette.

— Allow to air dry.

- o For peptides, small proteins and most compounds: A saturated solution of α-cyano-4-hydroxycinnamic acid in 50:50 ACN:H$_2$O with 0.1% TFA.

- o For proteins and other large molecules: a saturated solution of sinapinic acid in 50:50 ACN:H$_2$O with 0.1% TFA.

- o For glycopeptides/proteins and small compounds: a saturated solution of 2,5-dihydroxy benzoic acid (DHB) in 50:50 ACN:H$_2$O.

Alternatively, samples can be prepared in a stepwise manner. In the thin layer method, a homogeneous matrix "film" is formed on the target first, and the sample is then applied and absorbed by the matrix. This method yields good sensitivity, resolving power, and mass accuracy. Similarly, in the thick-layer method, nitrocellulose (NC) is used as the matrix additive; once a uniform NC-matrix layer is obtained on the target, the sample is applied. This preparation method suppresses alkali adduct formation and significantly increases the detection sensitivity, especially for peptides and proteins extracted from gels. The sandwich method is another variant in this category. A thin layer of matrix crystals is prepared as in the thin-layer method, followed by the subsequent addition of droplets of (a) aqueous 0.1% TFA, (b) sample and (c) matrix.

Desorption/Ionization on Silicon (DIOS)

DIOS is a matrix-free method that uses pulsed laser desorption/ionization on silicon (**Figure 1.16**). Structured silicon surfaces such as porous silicon or silicon nanowires are UV-absorbing semiconductors with a large surface area (hundreds of m^2/cm^3). For its application to laser desorption/ionization mass spectrometry, the structure of structured silicon provides a scaffold for retaining solvent and analyte molecules, and the UV absorptivity affords a mechanism for the transfer of the laser energy to the analyte. This fortuitous combination of characteristics allows DIOS to be useful for a large variety of biomolecules including peptides, carbohydrates, and small organic compounds of various types. Unlike other direct, matrix-free desorption techniques, DIOS enables desorption/ionization with little or no analyte degradation.

DIOS has a great deal in common with MALDI. Instrumentation and acquisition using DIOS-MS requires only minor adjustments to the MALDI setup; the chips are simply affixed to a machined MALDI plate and inserted into the spectrometer. The same wavelength of laser light (337 nm) typically employed in MALDI is effective for DIOS. While DIOS is comparable to MALDI with respect to its sensitivity, it has several advantages due to the lack of interfering matrix: low background in the low mass range; uniform deposition of aqueous samples; and simplified sample handling. In addition, the chip-based format can be adapted to automated sample handling, where the laser rapidly scans from spot to spot. DIOS could thus accelerate and simplify high-throughput analysis of low molecular weight compounds, as MALDI has done for macromolecules. Because the masses of many low molecular weight compounds can be measured, DIOS-MS can be applied to the analysis of small molecule transformations, both enzymatic and chemical.

In a number of recent advances with DIOS-MS, the modification of the silicon surface with fluorinated silyating reagents have allowed for ultra-high sensitivity in the yoctomole range (**Figure 1.16**).

Desorption/ Ionization on Silicon

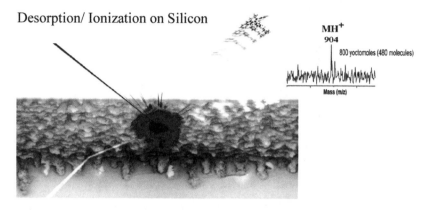

Figure 1.16. Desorption/Ionization on Silicon (DIOS) uses UV laser pulse from a structured silicon surface to generate intact gas phase ions. DIOS allows for small quantities of sample to be analyzed, 800 yoctomoles (480 molecules) of des-arg-bradykinin has been detected. In addition, DIOS mass spectrometry is useful for the analysis of heterogeneous samples and small molecules. On the left is a picture of a DIOS chip; the dark spots represent porous silicon. On the right is a diagrammatic representation of the DIOS event from a chip.

Fast Atom/Ion Bombardment

Fast atom ion bombardment, or FAB, is an ionization source similar to MALDI in that it uses a matrix and a highly energetic beam of particles to desorb ions from a surface. It is important, however, to point out the differences between MALDI and FAB. For MALDI, the energy beam is pulsed laser light, while FAB uses a continuous ion beam. With MALDI, the matrix is typically a solid crystalline, whereas FAB typically has a liquid matrix. It is also important to note that FAB is about 1000 times less sensitive than MALDI.

Fast Atom Bombardment

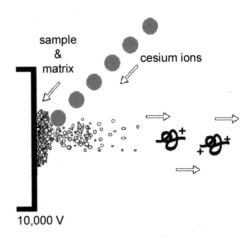

Figure 1.17. Fast atom bombardment (FAB) mass spectrometry, also known as liquid secondary ion mass spectrometry (LSIMS).

Fast atom bombardment is a soft ionization source which requires the use of a direct insertion probe for sample introduction, and a beam of Xe neutral atoms or Cs^+ ions to sputter the sample and matrix from the direct insertion probe surface. It is common to detect matrix ions in the FAB spectrum as well as the protonated or cationized (i.e. M + Na^+) molecular ion of the analyte of interest.

FAB matrix -- Facilitating the desorption and ionization process, the FAB matrix is a nonvolatile liquid material that serves to constantly replenish the surface with new sample as it is bombarded by the incident ion beam. By absorbing most of the incident energy, the matrix also minimizes sample degradation from the high-energy particle beam.

Two of the most common matrices used with FAB are m-nitrobenzyl alcohol and glycerol.

m-nitrobenzyl alcohol (NBA)

O_2N

—CH_2OH

glycerol

OH

HOH_2C—$\overset{|}{\underset{|}{C}}$—$CH_2OH$

H

The fast atoms or ions impinge on or collide with the matrix causing the matrix and analyte to be desorbed into the gas phase. The sample may already be charged and subsequently transferred into the gas phase by FAB, or it may become charged during FAB desorption through reactions with surrounding molecules or ions. Once in the gas phase, the charged molecules can be propelled electrostatically to the mass analyzer.

Electron Ionization

Electron ionization is one of the most important ionization sources for the routine analysis of small, hydrophobic, thermally stable molecules and is still widely used. Because EI usually generates numerous fragment ions it is a "hard" ionization source. However, the fragmentation information can also be very useful. For example, by employing databases containing over 200,000 electron ionization mass spectra, it is possible to identify an unknown compound in seconds (provided it exists in the database). These databases, combined with current computer storage capacity and searching algorithms, allow for rapid comparison with these databases (such as the NIST database), thus greatly facilitating the identification of small molecules.

Electron Ionization

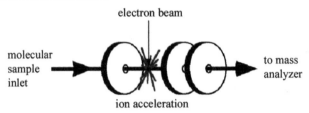

Figure 1.18. Electron ionization (EI) mass spectrometry

The electron ionization source is straightforward in design (**Figure 1.18**). The sample must be delivered as a gas which is accomplished by either "boiling off" the sample from a probe via thermal desorption, or by introduction of a gas through a capillary. The capillary is often the output of a capillary column from gas chromatography instrumentation. In this case, the capillary column provides separation (this is also known as gas chromatography mass spectrometry or GC/MS). Desorption of both solid and liquid samples is facilitated by heat as well as the vacuum of the mass spectrometer. Once in the gas phase the compound passes into an electron ionization source, where electrons excite the molecule, thus causing electron ejection ionization and fragmentation.

The utility of electron ionization decreases significantly for compounds above a molecular weight of 400 Da because the required thermal desorption of the sample often leads to thermal decomposition before vaporization is able to occur. The principal problems associated with thermal desorption in electron ionization are 1) involatility of large molecules, 2) thermal decomposition, and 3) excessive fragmentation.

The method, or mechanism, of electron ejection for positive ion formation proceeds as follows:

— The sample is thermally vaporized.

— Electrons ejected from a heated filament are accelerated through an electric field at 70 V to form a continuous electron beam.

— The sample molecule is passed through the electron beam.

— The electrons, containing 70 V of kinetic energy (70 electron volts or 70 eV), transfer some of their kinetic energy to the molecule. This transfer results in ionization (electron ejection) with the ion internally retaining usually no more than 6 eV excess energy.

$$M + e^- (70 \text{ eV}) \rightarrow M^+ (\tilde{\ }5 \text{ eV}) + 2e^- (\tilde{\ }65 \text{ eV})$$

— Excess internal energy (6 eV) in the molecule leads to some degree of fragmentation.

$$M^+ \rightarrow \text{molecular ions} + \text{fragment ions} + \text{neutral fragments}$$

Electron capture is usually much less efficient than electron ejection, yet it is sometimes used in the following way for high sensitivity work with compounds having a high electron affinity: $M + e^- \rightarrow M^-$.

Chemical Ionization

Chemical Ionization (CI) is applied to samples similar to those analyzed by EI and is primarily used to enhance the abundance of the molecular ion. Chemical ionization uses gas phase ion-molecule reactions within the vacuum of the mass spectrometer to produce ions from the sample molecule. The chemical ionization process is initiated with a reagent gas such as methane, isobutane, or ammonia, which is ionized by electron impact. High gas pressure in the ionization source results in ion-molecule reactions between the reagent gas ions and reagent gas neutrals. Some of the products of the ion-molecule reactions can react with the analyte molecules to produce ions.

A possible mechanism for ionization in CI occurs as follows:

$$\text{Reagent } (R) + e^- \rightarrow R^+ + 2\,e^-$$

$$R^+ + RH \rightarrow RH^+ + R$$

$$RH^+ + \text{Analyte } (A) \rightarrow AH^+ + R$$

In contrast to EI, an analyte is more likely to provide a molecular ion with reduced fragmentation using CI. However, similar to EI, samples must be thermally stable since vaporization within the CI source occurs through heating.

Negative chemical ionization (NCI) typically requires an analyte that contains electron-capturing moieties (e.g., fluorine atoms or nitrobenzyl groups). Such moieties significantly increase the sensitivity of NICI, in some cases 100 to 1000 times greater than that of electron ionization (EI). NCI is probably one of the most sensitive techniques and is used for a wide variety of small molecules with the caveat that the molecules are often chemically modified with an electron-capturing moiety prior to analysis.

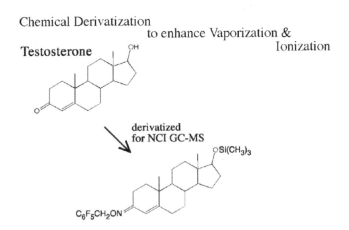

Chemical Derivatization
to enhance Vaporization &
Ionization

Testosterone

derivatized
for NCI GC-MS

Figure 1.19. The pentafluorobenzyl trimethyl silyl ether derivatives of steroids make them more amenable to high sensitivity measurements using negative chemical ionization.

While most compounds will not produce negative ions using EI or CI, many important compounds can produce negative ions and, in some cases, negative EI or CI mass spectrometry is more sensitive and selective than positive ion analysis. In fact, compounds like steroids are modified (**Figure 1.19**) to enhance NCI.

As mentioned, negative ions can be produced by electron capture, and in negative chemical ionization a buffer gas (such as methane) can slow down the electrons in the electron beam allowing them to be captured by the analyte molecules. The buffer gas also stabilizes the excited anions and reduces fragmentation. Therefore, NCI is in actuality an electron capture process and not what would traditionally be defined as a "chemical ionization" process.

Table 1.5. General Comparison of Ionization Sources.

Ionization Source	Typical Mass Range (Da)	Matrix Interference	Degradation	Complex Mixtures	LC/MS Amenable	Sensitivity
Electrospray Ionization (ESI)	70,000	none	none	somewhat limited	excellent	high femtomole to low picomole
Comments -	Excellent LC/MS tool; low salt tolerance (low millimolar); multiple charging useful, but significant suppression with mixtures occurs; low tolerance of mixtures; soft ionization (little fragmentation observed).					
NanoESI	70,000	none	none	somewhat limited but better than ESI	OK but low flow rates can present a problem	high zeptomole to low femtomole
Comments	Very sensitive and very low flow rates; applicable to LC/MS; but low flow rates require specialized systems; has reasonable salt tolerance (low millimolar); multiple charging useful but significant suppression can occur with mixtures; reasonable tolerance of mixtures; soft ionization (little fragmentation observed).					
APCI	1,200	none	thermal degradation	somewhat amenable	excellent	high femtomole
Comments	Excellent LC/MS tool; low salt tolerance (low millimolar); useful for hydrophobic materials.					
APPI	1,200	none	Photo dissociation	amenable	excellent	high femtomole
Comments	Excellent LC/MS tool; low salt tolerance (low millimolar); useful for hydrophobic materials.					
MALDI	300,000	yes	photo degradation and matrix reactions	good for complex mixtures	possible	low to high femtomole

(Continued)

Table 1.5. General Comparison of Ionization Sources. Continued

Ionization Source	Typical Mass Range (Da)	Matrix Interference	Degradation	Complex Mixtures	LC/MS Amenable	Sensitivity
Comments	Somewhat tolerant of salts; excellent sensitivity; matrix background can be problem for low mass ions; soft ionization (little fragmentation observed); photodegradation possible; suitable for complex mixtures. Limited multiple charging occurs so MS/MS data is not extensive.					
DIOS	3,000	None	photo degradation	good for complex mixtures	possible	Low femtomole to high yoctomole
Comments	Somewhat tolerant of salts; excellent sensitivity; soft ionization (little fragmentation observed); photodegradation possible; suitable for complex mixtures and small molecules.					
FAB	7,000	Yes	matrix reactions and some thermal degradation	somewhat amenable	very limited	nanomole
Comments	Relatively insensitive; little fragmentation; soft ionization; high salt tolerance to 0.01M, solubility with matrix required.					
Electron Ionization (EI)	500	none	Thermal	limited unless used with GC/MS	very limited	picomole
Comments	Good sensitivity; unique fragmentation data generated; National Institute of Science and Technology (NIST) database (>100,000 compounds) available to compare fragmentation data; thermal decomposition a major problem for biomolecules; limited mass range due to thermal desorption requirement.					
Chemical Ionization (CI)	500	none	thermal	limited unless used with GC/MS	very limited	picomole
Comments	Offers a softer ionization approach over EI yet still requires thermal desorption; negative CI particularly sensitive for perflourinated derivatives; a limited but powerful approach for certain derivatized molecules such as steroids.					

Summary

The mass spectrometer as a whole can be separated into distinct sections that include the sample inlet, ion source, mass analyzer, and detector. A sample is introduced into the mass spectrometer and is then ionized. The ion source produces ions either by electron ejection, electron capture, cationization, deprotonation or the transfer of a charged molecule from the condensed to the gas phase. MALDI and ESI have had a profound effect on mass spectrometry because they generate charged intact biomolecules into the gas phase. In comparison to other ionization sources such as APCI, EI, FAB, and CI, the techniques of MALDI and ESI have greatly extended the analysis capabilities of mass spectrometry to a wide range of compounds with detection capabilities ranging from the picomole to the zeptomole level.

Questions

- What are the primary disadvantages of electron ionization?

- What are some of the advantages of electron ionization?

- Why is it important to generate the intact ion?

- Why are ESI and MALDI effective at generating the intact ion?

- Why is ESI useful for studying noncovalent interactions?

- What is the purpose of the matrix in MALDI?

- Why is MALDI more tolerant of mixtures than ESI?

- What effect does multiple charging have on the mass-to-charge ratio (m/z)?

Useful References

Dole M, Mack LL, Hines RL, Mobley RC, Ferguson LD, Alice MB. *Molecular beams of macroions.* Journal of Chemical Physics. **1968**, 49:5, 2240.

Whitehouse CM, Dreyer RN, Yanashita M, Fenn JB. *Electrospray interface for liquid chromatographs and mass spectrometers.* Anal. Chem. **1985**, 57, 675-679.

Tanaka K, Waki H, Ido Y, Akita S, Yoshida Y, Yoshida T. *Protein and polymer analysis up to m/z 100,000 by laser ionization time-of-flight mass spectrometry.* Rapid Commun. Mass Spectrom. **1988**, 2, 151.

Karas M & Hillenkamp F. *Laser desorption ionization of proteins with molecular mass exceeding 10,000 Daltons.* Anal. Chem. **1988**, 60, 2299.

Bruins AP. *Mechanistic aspects of electrospray ionization.* J. Chromatogr. A, **1998**, 795, 345-357.

Fenn JB, Mann M, Meng CK, Wong SF, Whitehouse CM. *Electrospray ionization - principles and practice.* Mass Spectrometry Reviews. **1990**, 9, 37.

McLafferty FW & Turecek F. *Interpretation of Mass Spectra.* 4th ed. Mill Valley, Calif. : University Science Books, **1993**.

Cole R (Editor). *Electrospray Ionization Mass Spectrometry: Fundamentals, Instrumentation, and Applications.* New York: Wiley and Sons, **1997**.

Cole RB. *Some tenets pertaining to electrospray ionization mass spectrometry.* J. Mass Spectrom. **2000**, 35, 763-772.

Kebarle P. *A brief overview of the present status of the mechanisms involved in electrospray mass spectrometry.* J. Mass Spectrom. **2000**, 35, 804-817.

Gaskell SJ. *Electrospray: principles and practice.* J. Mass Spectrom. **2000**, 35, 677-688.

Cech NB and Enke CG. *Practical implications of some recent studies in electrospray ionization fundamentals.* Mass Spectrom. Rev. **2001**, 20, 362-387.

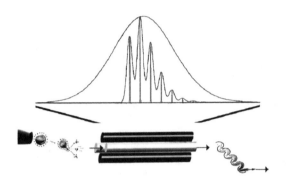

Chapter 2
Mass Analyzers

Knowledge becomes wisdom only after it has
been put to practical use. — Unknown

Perspective

With the advent of ionization sources that can vaporize and ionize biomolecules, it has become necessary to improve mass analyzer performance with respect to speed, accuracy, and resolution (**Figure 2.1**). More specifically, quadrupoles, quadrupole ion traps, time-of-flight (TOF), time-of-flight reflectron, and ion cyclotron resonance (ICR) mass analyzers have undergone numerous modifications/improvements over the past decade in order to be interfaced with MALDI and ESI. The biggest challenge came in the ionization of interfacing atmospheric pressure sources (760 torr) to analyzers maintained at 10^{-6} to 10^{-11} torr, a remarkable pressure differential of more than 9 orders of magnitude. This chapter will focus on the principles of operation and current performance capabilities of mass analyzers, while briefly touching on ion detectors and the concept of vacuum in a mass spectrometer.

Mass Analysis

Analytical instruments in general have variations in their capabilities as a result of their individual design and intended purpose. This is also true for mass spectrometers. While all mass spectrometers rely on a mass analyzer, not all analyzers operate in the same way; some separate ions in space while others separate ions by time. In the most general terms, a mass analyzer measures gas phase ions with respect to their mass-to-charge ratio (m/z), where the charge is produced by the addition or loss of a proton(s), cation(s), anion(s) or electron(s). The addition of charge allows the molecule to be affected by electric fields thus allowing its mass measurement. This is an important aspect to remember about mass analyzers -- they measure the *m/z* ratio, not the mass. It is often a point of confusion because if an ion has multiple charges, the *m/z* will be significantly less than the actual mass (**Figures 1.8 and 1.9**). For example, a doubly charged peptide ion of mass 976.5 Daltons (Da) ($C_{37}H_{68}N_{16}O_{14}^{2+}$) has an *m/z* of 488.3.

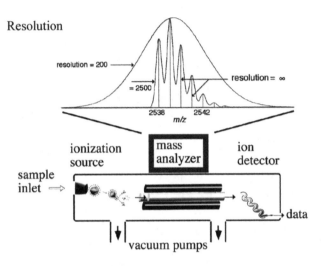

Figure 2.1. The effect of resolution upon mass accuracy. The overlaid spectra were calculated for the same molecular formula ($C_{101}H_{145}N_{34}O_{44}$) at resolutions of 200, 2500, and infinity (∞).

Multiple charging is especially common with electrospray ionization, yielding numerous peaks that correspond to the same species yet are observed at different *m/z*.

The first mass analyzers, made in the early 1900's, used magnetic fields to separate ions according to their radius of curvature through the magnetic field. The design of modern analyzers has changed significantly in the last five years, now offering much higher accuracy, increased sensitivity, broader mass range, and the ability to give structural information. Because ionization techniques have evolved, mass analyzers have been forced to change in order to meet the demands of analyzing a wide range of biomolecular ions with part per million mass accuracy and sub femtomole sensitivity. The characteristics (**Table 2.1**) of these mass analyzers will be covered in this chapter.

Table 2.1

Mass Analyzers	Event
Quadrupole	scan radio frequency field
Quadrupole Ion Trap	scan radio frequency field
Time-of-Flight (TOF)	time-of-flight correlated directly to ion's m/z
Time-of-Flight Reflectron	time-of-flight correlated directly to ion's m/z
Quad-TOF	radio frequency field scanning and time-of-flight
Magnetic Sector	magnetic field affects radius of curvature of ions
Fourier Transform Ion Cyclotron Resonance MS	translates ion cyclotron motion to m/z (FTMS)

Performance Characteristics

The performance of a mass analyzer can typically be defined by the following characteristics: accuracy, resolution, mass range, tandem analysis capabilities, and scan speed.

Accuracy

This is the ability with which the analyzer can accurately provide m/z information and is largely a function of an instrument's stability and resolution. For example, an instrument with 0.01% accuracy can provide information on a 1000 Da peptide to ±0.1 Da or a 10,000 Da protein to ±1.0 Da. The accuracy varies dramatically from analyzer to analyzer depending on the analyzer type and resolution. An alternative means of describing accuracy is using part per million (ppm) terminology, where 1000 Da peptide to ±0.1 Da could also be described as 1000.00 Da peptide to ± 100 ppm.

Resolution (Resolving Power)

Resolution is the ability of a mass spectrometer to distinguish between ions of different mass-to-charge ratios. Therefore, greater resolution corresponds directly to the increased ability to differentiate ions. The most common definition of resolution is given by the following equation:

Resolution = M/ΔM   Equation 2.1

where M corresponds to *m/z* and ΔM represents the full width at half maximum (FWHM). An example of resolution measurement is shown in **Figure 2.2** where the peak has an *m/z* of 500 and a FWHM of 1. The resulting resolution is M/ΔM = 500/1 = 500.

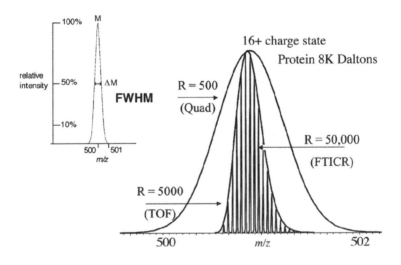

Figure 2.2. The resolution is determined by the measurement of peak's *m/z* and FWHM, in this case *m/z* = 500 and the FWHM = 1.

The analyzer's resolving power does, to some extent, determine the accuracy of a particular instrument, as characterized in

Figure 2.2. The average mass of a molecule is calculated using the weighted average mass of all isotopes of each constituent element of the molecule. The monoisotopic mass is calculated using the mass of the elemental isotope having the greatest abundance for each constituent element. If an instrument cannot resolve the isotopes it will generate a broad peak with the center representing the average mass. Higher resolution can offer the benefits of separating an ion's individual isotopes or the narrowing of peaks allows a more accurate determination of its position.

Mass Range

This is the *m/z* range of the mass analyzer. For instance, quadrupole analyzers typically scan up to *m/z* 3000. A magnetic sector analyzer typically scans up to *m/z* 10,000 and time-of-flight analyzers have virtually unlimited *m/z* range.

Tandem Mass Analysis (MS/MS or MS^n)

This is the ability of the analyzer to separate different molecular ions, generate fragment ions from a selected ion, and then mass measure the fragmented ions. The fragmented ions are used for structural determination of original molecular ions.

Typically, tandem MS experiments are performed by colliding a selected ion with inert gas molecules such as argon or helium, and the resulting fragments are mass analyzed. Tandem mass analysis is used to sequence peptides, and structurally characterize carbohydrates, small oligo-nucleotides, and lipids.

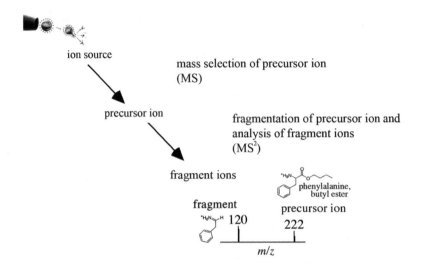

Scheme 2.1. Tandem mass spectrometry analysis.

The term "tandem" mass analysis comes from the events being either tandem in space or tandem in time. Tandem mass analysis in space is performed by consecutive analyzers whereas tandem mass analysis in time is performed with the same analyzer, which isolates the ion of interest, fragments it, and analyzes the fragment ions. Tandem analysis characteristics are summarized for the different analyzers in **Table 2.2**.

Scan Speed

This refers to the rate at which the analyzer scans over a particular mass range. Most instruments require seconds to perform a full scan, however this can vary widely depending on the analyzer. Time-of-flight analyzers, for example, complete analyses in milliseconds or less.

Mass Analyzers

It is clear from Chapter 1 that ESI and MALDI are quite different in terms of how ions are generated. ESI creates ions in a continuous stream from charged droplets under atmospheric pressure conditions and ions are created in a continuous stream, for these reasons quadrupoles presented an well-suited analyzer for ESI since they are both tolerant of relatively high pressures ($\sim 10^{-5}$ torr) and they are capable of continuously scanning the ESI ion stream. MALDI, on the other hand, generates ions from short, nanosecond laser pulses and is readily compatible with time-of-flight mass analysis, which measures precisely timed ion packets such as those generated from a laser pulse. The most common analyzers are discussed in this section with a description of their respective advantages and disadvantages.

Quadrupoles

Quadrupole mass analyzers (**Figure 2.3**) have been used with EI sources since the 1950's and are still the most common mass analyzers in existence today. Interestingly, quadrupole mass analyzers have found new utility in their capacity to interface with ESI and APCI. Quadrupoles offer three main advantages. They tolerate relatively high pressures. Secondly, quadrupoles have a significant mass range with the capability of analyzing up to an *m/z* of 4000, which is useful because electrospray ionization of proteins and other biomolecules commonly produce charge distributions from *m/z* 1000 to 3500. Finally, quadrupole mass spectrometers are relatively low cost instruments. Considering the mutually complementary features of ESI and quadrupoles, it is not surprising that the first successful commercial electrospray instruments were coupled with quadrupole mass analyzers.

Quadrupole Mass Analyzer

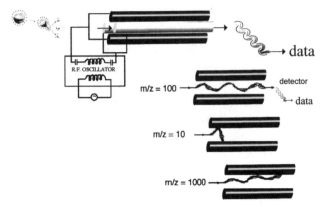

Figure 2.3. Schematic diagram showing arrangement of quadrupole rods and electrical connection to RF generator; a DC potential (not shown) is also superimposed on the rods. A cross-section of a quadrupole mass analyzer taken as it analyzes for m/z 100, 10, and 1000, respectively. It is important to note that both the DC and RF fields are the same in all three cases and only ions with $m/z = 100$ (top example) traverse the total length of the quadrupole and reach the detector; the other ions are filtered out.

Quadrupole mass analyzers are connected in parallel to a radio frequency (RF) generator and a DC potential. At a specific RF field, only ions of a specific m/z can pass through the quadrupoles as shown in **Figure 2.3**, where only the ion of m/z 100 is detected. In all three cases in **Figure 2.3** the DC and RF fields are the same. Therefore by scanning the RF field a broad m/z range (typically 100 to 4000) can be achieved in approximately one second.

In order to perform tandem mass analysis with a quadrupole instrument, it is necessary to place three quadrupoles in series. Each quadrupole has a separate function: the first quadrupole (Q1) is used to scan across a preset m/z range and select an ion of interest. The second quadrupole (Q2), also known as the collision cell, focuses and transmits the ions while introducing a collision gas (argon or helium) into the flight path of the selected ion. The third quadrupole (Q3) serves to analyze the fragment ions generated in the collision cell (Q2) (**Figure 2.4**). A stepwise example of collision-induced dissociation (CID), is shown in **Scheme 2.1**.

Tandem Mass Spectrometry (MS/MS) with a triple quadrupole

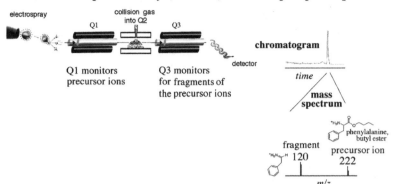

Figure 2.4. A triple quadrupole ESI mass spectrometer possesses ion selection and fragmentation capabilities allowing for tandem mass spectra.

Quadrupole Ion Trap

The ion trap mass analyzer shown in **Figure 2.5** (roughly the size of a tennis ball) was conceived at the same time as the quadrupole mass analyzer by the same person, Wolfgang Paul. Incidentally, the physics behind both of these analyzers is similar. However, in an ion trap, rather than passing through a quadrupole analyzer with a superimposed radio frequency field, the ions are trapped in a radio frequency quadrupole field. One method of using an ion trap for mass spectrometry involves generating ions internally with EI, followed by mass analysis. Another, more popular, method of using an ion trap for mass spectrometry involves generating ions externally with ESI or MALDI and using ion optics for sample injection into the trapping volume. The quadrupole ion trap typically consists of a ring electrode and two hyperbolic endcap electrodes (**Figure 2.5**). The motion of the ions induced by the electric field on these electrodes allows ions to be trapped or ejected from the ion trap. In the normal mode, the radio frequency is scanned to resonantly excite and therefore eject ions through small holes in the endcap to a detector. As the RF is scanned to higher frequencies, higher m/z ions are excited, ejected, and detected.

A very useful feature of ion traps is that it is possible to isolate one ion species by ejecting all others from the trap. The

47

isolated ions can subsequently be fragmented by collisional activation and the fragments detected. The primary advantage of quadrupole ion traps is that multiple collision induced dissociation experiments can be performed quickly without having multiple analyzers, such that real time LC-MS/MS is now routine. Other important advantages of quadrupole ion traps include their compact size, and their ability to trap and accumulate ions to provide a better ion signal.

Quadrupole ion traps have been utilized in a number of applications ranging from electrospray ionization MS^n (**Figure 2.5**) of biomolecules to their more recent interface with MALDI. MS^n allows for multiple MS/MS experiments to be performed on subsequent fragment ions, providing additional fragmentation information. Yet, ion traps most important application has been in the characterization of proteins. LC-MS/MS experiments are performed on proteolytic digests which provide both MS and MS/MS information. This information allows for protein identification and post-translational modification characterization. The mass range (~4000 *m/z*) of commercial LC-traps is well matched to *m/z* values generated from the electrospray ionization of peptides and the resolution allows for charge state identification of multiply-charged peptide ions. Quadrupole ion trap mass spectrometers can analyze peptides from a tryptic digest present at the 20-100 fmol level. Another asset of the ion trap technique for peptide analysis is the ability to perform multiple stages of mass spectrometry, which can significantly increase the amount of structural information.

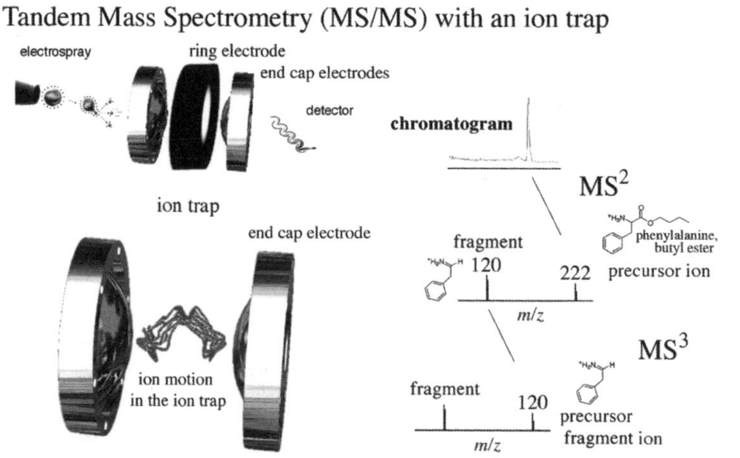

Tandem Mass Spectrometry (MS/MS) with an ion trap

Figure 2.5. Ions inside a 3D ion trap mass analyzer can be analyzed to produce a mass spectrum, or a particular ion can be trapped inside and made to undergo collisions to produce fragmentation information.

Linear Ion Trap

The linear ion trap differs from the 3D ion trap (**Figure 2.6**) as it confines ions along the axis of a quadrupole mass analyzer using a two-dimensional (2D) radio frequency (RF) field with potentials applied to end electrodes. The primary advantage to the linear trap over the 3D trap is the larger analyzer volume lends itself to a greater dynamic ranges and an improved range of quantitative analysis.

Quadrupole Linear Ion Trap Mass Analyzer

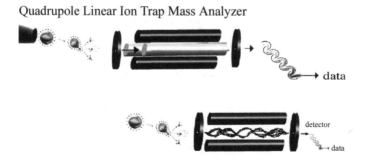

Figure 2.6. A linear ion trap mass analyzer confines the ions along the axis of quadrupoles using a 2D radio frequency and stopping potentials on the end electrodes.

Ion Trap's Limitations: Precursor ion scanning, "1/3 rule" & Dynamic range

Given the power of the ion trap the major limitations of this device that keep it from being the ultimate tool for pharmacokinetics and proteomics include the following: 1) the ability to perform high sensitivity triple quadrupole-type precursor ion scanning and neutral loss scanning experiments is not possible with ion traps. 2) The upper limit on the ratio between precursor m/z and the lowest trapped fragment ion is ~0.3 (also known as the "one third rule"). An example of the one third rule is that fragment ions of m/z 900 will not be detected below m/z 300, presenting a significant limitation for *de novo* sequencing of peptides. 3) The dynamic range of ion traps are limited because when too many ions are in the trap, space charge effects diminish the performance of the ion trap analyzer. To get around this, automated scans can rapidly count ions before they go into the trap, therefore limiting the number of ions getting in. Yet this approach presents a problem when an ion of interest is accompanied by a large background ion population.

Double-Focusing Magnetic Sector

The earliest mass analyzers separated ions with a magnetic field. In magnetic analysis, the ions are accelerated into a magnetic field using an electric field. A charged particle traveling through a magnetic field will travel in a circular motion with a radius that depends on the speed of the ion, the magnetic field strength, and the ion's m/z. A mass spectrum is obtained by scanning the magnetic field and monitoring ions as they strike a fixed point detector. A limitation of magnetic analyzers is their relatively low resolution. In order to improve this, magnetic instruments were modified with the addition of an electrostatic analyzer to focus the ions. These are called double-sector or two-sector instruments. The electric sector serves as a kinetic energy focusing element allowing only ions of a particular kinetic energy to pass through its field irrespective of their mass-to-charge ratio. Thus, the addition of an electric sector allows only ions of uniform kinetic energy to reach the detector, thereby decreasing the kinetic energy spread, which in turn increases resolution. It should be noted that the corresponding increase in resolution does have its costs in terms of sensitivity. These double-focusing (**Figure 2.7**) mass analyzers are used with ESI, FAB and EI ionization, however they are not widely used today primarily due to their large size and the success of time-of-flight, quadrupole and FTMS analyzers with ESI and MALDI.

Magentic Sector Mass Analyzer

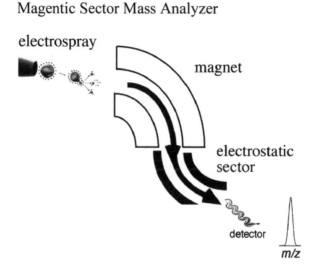

Figure 2.7. A two-sector double-focusing instrument.

Quadrupole Time-of-Flight Tandem MS

The linear time-of-flight (TOF) mass analyzer (**Figure 2.7**) is the simplest mass analyzer. It has enjoyed a renaissance with the invention of MALDI and its recent application to electrospray and even gas chromatography electron ionization mass spectrometry (GC/MS). Time-of-flight analysis is based on accelerating a group of ions to a detector where all of the ions are given the same amount of energy through an accelerating potential. Because the ions have the same energy, but a different mass, the lighter ions reach the detector first because of their greater velocity, while the heavier ions take longer due to their heavier masses and lower velocity. Hence, the analyzer is called time-of-flight because the mass is determined from the ions' time of arrival. Mass, charge, and kinetic energy of the ion all play a part in the arrival time at the detector. Since the kinetic energy (KE) of the ion is equal to $1/2\ mv^2$, the ion's velocity can be represented as $v = d/t = (2KE/m)^{1/2}$. The ions will travel a given distance d, within a time t, where t is dependent upon the mass-to-charge ratio (*m/z*). In this equation, $v = d/t = (2KE/m)^{1/2}$, assuming that z = 1. Another representation of this equation to more clearly present how mass is determined is $m = 2t^2\ KE/d^2$ where KE is constant.

Time-of-Flight Mass Analyzer

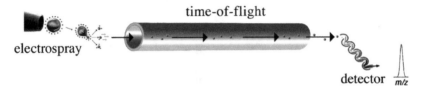

Figure 2.8. Time-of-flight and time-of-flight reflectron mass analyzers. The TOF analyzer has virtually unlimited mass range, while the TOF reflectron has mass range up to *m/z* ~10,000. It should be noted that most detectors have a limited mass range.

The time-of-flight (TOF) reflectron (**Figure 2.8**) is now widely used for ESI, MALDI, and more recently for electron ionization in GC/MS applications. It combines time-of-flight technology with an electrostatic mirror. The reflectron serves to increase the amount of time (t) ions need to reach the detector while reducing their kinetic energy distribution, thereby reducing the temporal distribution Δt. Since resolution is defined by the mass of a peak divided by the width of a peak or $m/\Delta m$ (or $t/\Delta t$ since m is related to t), increasing t and decreasing Δt results in higher resolution. Therefore, the TOF reflectron offers high resolution over a simple TOF instrument by increasing the path length and kinetic energy focusing through the reflectron. It should be noted that the increased resolution (typically above 5000) and sensitivity on a TOF reflectron does decrease significantly at higher masses (typically above 5000 *m/z*).

Another type of tandem mass analysis, MS/MS, is also possible with MALDI TOF reflectron mass analyzers. MS/MS is accomplished by taking advantage of MALDI fragmentation that occurs following ionization, or post-source decay (PSD). Time-of-flight instruments alone will not separate post-ionization fragment ions from the same precursor ion because both the precursor and fragment ions have the same velocity and thus reach the detector at the same time. The reflectron takes advantage of the fact that the fragment ions have different kinetic energies and separates them based on how deeply the ions penetrate the reflectron field, thus producing a fragment ion spectrum (**Figure 2.9** and **2.10**).

Time-of-Flight Reflectron Mass Analyzer

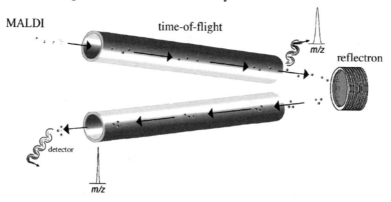

Figure 2.9. A MALDI time-of-flight reflectron mass analyzer and its ability to improve resolution over time-of-flight analysis with the reflectron. The TOF reflectron mass analyzer with an ESI ion source has also gained wide use due to the fast acquisition rates (milliseconds), good mass range (up to ~10,000 m/z) and accuracy on the order of 5 part per million (ppm).

It should be noted that electrospray has also been adapted to TOF reflectron analyzers, where the ions from the continuous ESI source can be stored in the hexapole (or octapole) ion guide then pulsed into the TOF analyzer. Thus, the necessary electrostatic pulsing creates a time zero from which the TOF measurements can begin.

Time-of-Flight Reflectron Mass Analyzer

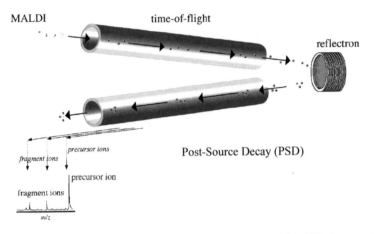

Figure 2.10. A MALDI time-of-flight reflectron mass analyzer and its ability to generate fragmentation information. Fragmentation analysis from a MALDI TOF reflectron is known as post-source decay or PSD.

The MALDI with Time-of-Flight Analysis

In the initial stages of MALDI–TOF development, these instruments had relatively poor resolution which severely limited their accuracy. An innovation that has had a dramatic effect on increasing the resolving power of MALDI time-of-flight instruments has been delayed extraction (DE), as shown in **Figure 2.11**. In theory, delayed extraction is a relatively simple means of cooling and focusing the ions immediately after the MALDI ionization event, yet in practice it was initially a challenge to pulse 10,000 volts on and off within a nanosecond time scale. In traditional MALDI instruments, the ions were accelerated out of the ionization source immediately as they were formed. However, with delayed extraction the ions are allowed to "cool" for ~150 nanoseconds before being accelerated to the analyzer. This cooling period generates a set of ions with a much smaller kinetic energy distribution, ultimately reducing the temporal spread of ions once they enter the TOF analyzer. Overall, this results in increased resolution and accuracy. The benefits of delayed extraction significantly diminish with larger macromolecules such as proteins (>30,000 Da).

Delayed Extraction with MALDI

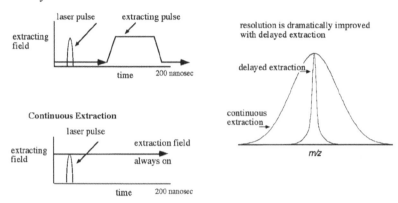

Figure 2.11. Delayed extraction (DE) is a technique applied in MALDI which allows ions to be extracted from the ionization source after a cooling period of ~150 nanoseconds. This cooling period effectively narrows the kinetic energy distribution of the ions, thus providing higher resolution than in continuous extraction techniques.

Quadrupole Time-of-Flight MS

Quadrupole-TOF mass analyzers are typically coupled to electrospray ionization sources and more recently they have been successfully coupled to MALDI. The ESI quad-TOF (**Figure 2.12**) combines the stability of a quadrupole analyzer with the high efficiency, sensitivity, and accuracy of a time-of-flight reflectron mass analyzer. The quadrupole can act as any simple quadrupole analyzer to scan across a specified m/z range. However, it can also be used to selectively isolate a precursor ion and direct that ion into the collision cell. The resultant fragment ions are then analyzed by the TOF reflectron mass analyzer. Quadrupole-TOF exploits the quadrupole's ability to select a particular ion and the ability of TOF-MS to achieve simultaneous and accurate measurements of ions across the full mass range. This is in contrast to conventional analyzers, such as tandem quadrupoles, which must scan over one mass at a time. Quadrupole-TOF analyzers offer significantly higher sensitivity and accuracy over tandem quadrupole instruments when acquiring full fragment mass spectra.

The quadrupole-TOF instrument can use either the quadrupole or TOF analyzers independently or together for tandem MS experiments. The TOF component of the instrument has an upper m/z limit in excess of 10,000. The high resolving power (~10,000) of the TOF also enables good mass measurement accuracy on the 10 ppm level. Due to its high accuracy and sensitivity, the ESI quad-TOF mass spectrometer is being incorporated into both proteomics and pharmacokinetics problem solving.

Quadrupole Time-of-Flight Mass Analyzer

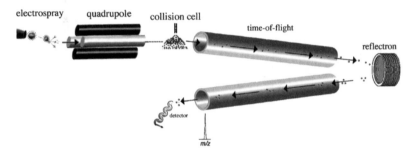

Figure 2.12. An electrospray ionization quadrupole time-of-flight mass spectrometer.

Fourier Transform Mass Spectrometry (FTMS)

FTMS is based on the principle of monitoring a charged particle's orbiting motion in a magnetic field (**Figure 2.13-14**). While the ions are orbiting, a pulsed radio frequency (RF) signal is used to excite them. This RF excitation allows the ions to produce a detectable image current by bringing them into coherent motion and enlarging the radius of the orbit. The image current generated by all of the ions can then be Fourier-transformed to obtain the component frequencies of the different ions, which correspond to their m/z. Because the frequencies can be obtained with high accuracy, their corresponding m/z can also be calculated with high accuracy. It is important to note that a signal is generated only by the coherent motion of ions under ultra-high vacuum conditions (10^{-11} – 10^{-9} Torr). This signal has to be measured for a minimum time (typically 500 ms to 1 second) to provide high resolution. As pressure increases, signal decays faster due to loss of coherent motion due to collisions (e.g. in ~ <150 ms) and does not allow for high resolution measurements (**Figure 2.14**).

Fourier transform ion cyclotron resonance mass analyzer

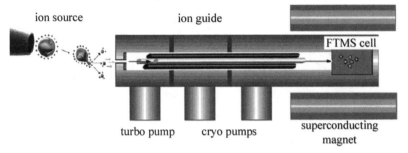

Figure 2.13. A side view of an FTMS instrument with ESI source. The ESI ions are formed and guided into the analyzer cell using a single stage quadrupole rod assembly. The analyzer cell rests in the superconducting magnet (diagram courtesy IonSpec Corporation).

Ions undergoing coherent cyclotron motion between two electrodes are illustrated in **Figure 2.13**. As the positively charged ions move away from the top electrode and closer to the bottom electrode, the electric field of the ions induces electrons in the external circuit to flow and accumulate on the bottom electrode. On the other half of the cyclotron orbit, the electrons leave the bottom electrode and accumulate on the top electrode as the ions approach. The oscillating flow of electrons in the external circuit is called an image current. When a mixture of ions with different m/z values are all simultaneously accelerated, the image current signal at the output of the amplifier is a composite transient signal with frequency components representing each m/z value. In short, all of the ions trapped in the analyzer cell are excited into a higher cyclotron orbit, using a radio frequency pulse. The composite transient image current signal of the ions as they relax is acquired by a computer and a Fourier transform is used to separate out the individual cyclotron frequencies. The effect of pressure on the signal and resolution is demonstrated in **Figure 2.14**.

Ion Cyclotron Motion with Fourier transform

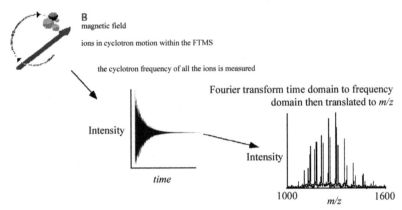

Figure 2.14. ESI FTMS data generated on multiple proteins, the sinusoidal composite image current for all *m/z* ions can be Fourier transformed to measure frequencies (and therefore *m/z*) accurately.

In addition to high resolution, FTMS also offers the ability to perform multiple collision experiments (MS^n). FTMS is capable of ejecting all but the ion of interest. The selected ion is then subjected to a collision gas (or another form of excitation such as laser light or electron capture) to induce fragmentation. Mass analysis can then be carried out on the fragments to generate a fragmentation spectrum. The high resolution of FTMS/MS also yields high-accuracy fragment masses.

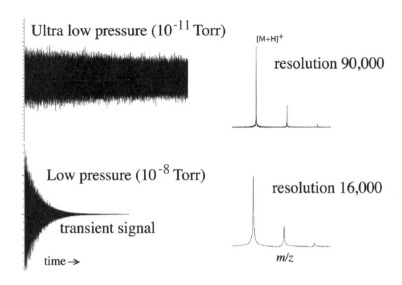

Figure 2.15. Pressure effect on transient signal and resolution.

FTMS is a relative neophyte to biomolecular analysis, yet many of its advantages are generating more and more interest. It is now becoming more common to couple ultrahigh resolution (>10^5) FTMS to a wide variety of ionization sources, including MALDI, ESI, APCI, and EI. The result of an FTMS analyzer's high resolving power is high accuracy (often at the part per million level) as illustrated for a protein in **Figure 2.15** where individual isotopes can be observed. The Fourier transform of the ICR signal greatly enhances the utility of ICR by simultaneously measuring all the overlaying frequencies produced by the ions within the ICR cell. The individual frequencies can then be easily and accurately translated into the ion's *m/z*.

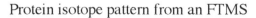

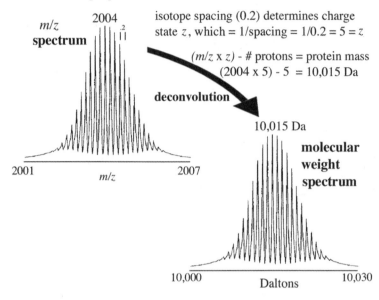

Figure 2.16. A demonstration of deconvolution from an FTMS mass spectrum of a 10 KDa protein at a resolution of 30,000. The cluster of peaks represents the isotope distribution of a protein and the 0.2 *m/z* isotope spacing indicates a 5+ charge state.

In general, increasing magnetic field (B) has a favorable effect on performance. The Fourier transform of the ICR signal, by measuring overlaying frequencies simultaneously, allows for high resolution and high mass accuracy without compromising sensitivity. This is in sharp contrast to double sector instruments that suffer from a loss in sensitivity at the highest resolution and accuracy. The high resolution capabilities of FTMS are directly related to the magnetic field of the FTMS superconducting magnet, with the resolution increasing as a linear function of the field. The ion capacity as well as MS/MS kinetic energy experiments increases as a square of the magnetic therefore improving dynamic range and fragmentation data. One challenge in increasing B is the magnetic mirror effect where ion transmission to the inside of magnetic field becomes more difficult due to magnetic field lines. Also, manufacturing high field magnets with larger bores and excellent field homogeneity (in the ICR housing) becomes technically more difficult.

FTMS instrumentation is affected by the magnetic field in the following ways:

FTMS attribute	Effect of Magnetic Field Strength (B)	What it means:
Resolution (m/Δm)	Directly proportional to **B**	Improves mass accuracy and the ability to get isotopic resolution on large macromolecules
Kinetic Energy	Directly proportional to **B²**	Increases the fragmentation and also ability to fragment larger macromolecules
Ion capacity	Directly proportional to **B²**	Can store more ions before space–charge adversely affects performance

Ion cyclotron resonance

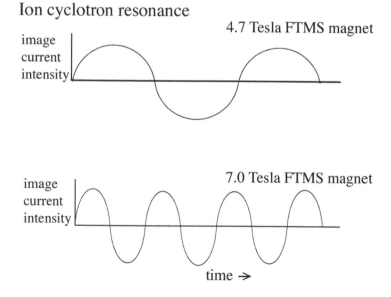

Figure 2.17. Fourier transform ion cyclotron frequency increases with magnetic field strength. The increased frequency improves accuracy as it allows for more measurements to average.

Because ion frequency = K*B*z/m, larger magnetic fields provide a higher frequency for the same *m/z*, therefore more data points are generated to define the frequency more precisely which ultimately increases accuracy (**Figure 2.17**).

Quadrupole-FTMS and quadrupole linear ion trap-FTMS mass analyzers that have recently been introduced are typically coupled to electrospray ionization sources. The quad-FTMS combines the stability of a quadrupole analyzer with the high accuracy of a FTMS. The quadrupole can act as any simple quadrupole analyzer to scan across a specified *m/z* range. However, it can also be used to selectively isolate a precursor ion and direct that ion into the collision cell or the FTMS. The resultant precursor and fragment ions can then be analyzed by the FTMS.

Performing MS/MS experiments outside the magnet presents some advantages since high resolution in FTMS is dependent on the presence of high vacuum. MS/MS experiments involve collisions at a transiently high pressure (10^{-6} – 10^{-7} Torr) that then has to be reduced to achieve high resolution (10^{-10} – 10^{-9} Torr). Performing MS/MS experiments outside the cell is thus faster since the ICR cell can be maintained at ultra-high vacuum. This makes the newer hybrid instrument designs are optimum over coupling FTMS/MS to separation techniques such as LC.

Table 2.2. A general comparison of mass analyzers typically used for electrospray. These values vary with instrument manufacturer.

	Quadrupole	Ion Trap	Time-of-Flight	Time-of-Flight Reflectron	Magnetic Sector	FTMS	Quadrupole - TOF
Accuracy	0.01% (100 ppm)	0.01% (100 ppm)	0.02 to 0.2% (200 ppm)	0.001% (10 ppm)	<0.0005% (<5 ppm)	<0.0005% (<5 ppm)	0.001% (10 ppm)
Resolution	4000	4000	8000	15,000	30,000	100,000	10,000
m/z Range	4000	4000	>300,000	10,000	10,000	10,000	10,000
Scan Speed	~ a second	~ a second	milliseconds	milliseconds	~ a second	~ a second	~ a second
Tandem MS	MS^2 (triple quad)	MS^n	MS	MS^2	MS^2	MS^n	MS^2
Tandem MS Comments	Good accuracy Good resolution Low-energy collisions	Good accuracy Good resolution Low-energy collisions	Not generally applicable	Precursor ion selection is limited to a wide mass range; growing number of applications	Limited resolution High-energy collisions	Excellent accuracy & resolution of product ions	Excellent accuracy Good resolution Low-energy collisions High sensitivity
General Comments	Low cost Ease of switching pos/neg ions	Low cost Ease of switching pos/neg ions Well-suited MS^n	Low cost	Good accuracy Good resolution	Instrument is massive Capable of high resolution	High Res, MS^n high vacuum, superconducting magnet, expense	Known for high sensitivity & accuracy when used for MS^2

Detectors

Once the ions are separated by the mass analyzer, they reach the ion detector (**Figures 2.1** and **2.18-21**), which generates a current signal from the incident ions. The most commonly used detector is the electron multiplier, which transfers the kinetic energy of incident ions to a surface that in turn generates secondary electrons. However, a variety of approaches are used to detect ions depending on the type of mass spectrometer.

Electron Multiplier

Perhaps the most common means of detecting ions involves an electron multiplier (**Figure 2.18**), which is made up of a series (12 to 24) of aluminum oxide (Al_2O_3) dynodes maintained at ever increasing potentials. Ions strike the first dynode surface causing an emission of electrons. These electrons are then attracted to the next dynode held at a higher potential and therefore more secondary electrons are generated. Ultimately, as numerous dynodes are involved, a cascade of electrons is formed that results in an overall current gain on the order of one million or higher.

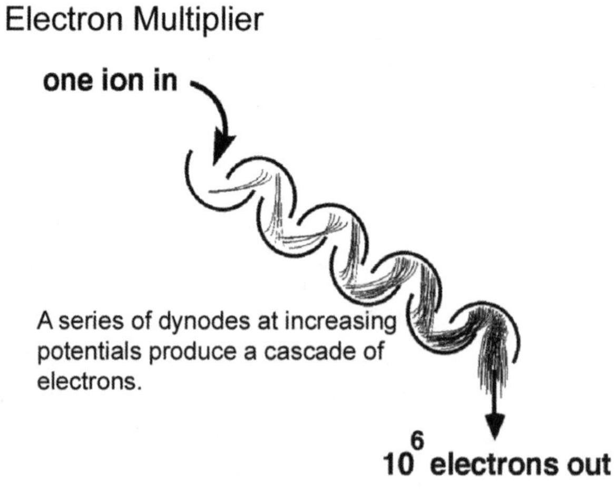

Electron Multiplier

one ion in

A series of dynodes at increasing potentials produce a cascade of electrons.

10^6 **electrons out**

Figure 2.18. Diagrammatic representation of an electron multiplier and the cascade of electrons that results in a 106 amplification of current in a mass spectrometer.

The high energy dynode (HED) uses an accelerating electrostatic field to increase the velocity of the ions. Since the signal on an electron multiplier is highly dependent on ion velocity, the HED serves to increase signal intensity and therefore sensitivity.

Faraday Cup

A Faraday cup (**Figure 2.19**) involves an ion striking the dynode (BeO, GaP, or CsSb) surface which causes secondary electrons to be ejected. This temporary electron emission induces a positive charge on the detector and therefore a current of electrons flowing toward the detector. This detector is not particularly sensitive, offering limited amplification of signal, yet it is tolerant of relatively high pressure.

Faraday cup

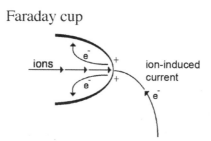

Figure 2.19. Faraday cup converts the striking ion into a current by temporarily emitting electrons creating a positive charge and the adsorption of the charge from the ion striking the detector.

Photomultiplier Conversion Dynode

The photomultiplier conversion dynode detector (**Figure 2.20**) is not as commonly used at the electron multiplier yet it is similar in design where the secondary electrons strike a phosphorus screen instead of a dynode. The phosphorus screen releases photons which are detected by the photomultiplier. Photomultipliers also operate like the electron multiplier where the striking of the photon on a scintillating surface results in the release of electrons that are then amplified using the cascading principle. One advantage of the conversion dynode is that the photomultiplier tube is sealed in a vacuum, unexposed to the environment of the mass spectrometer and thus the possibility of contamination is removed. This improves the lifetimes of these detectors over electron multipliers. A five-year or greater lifetime is typical, and they have a similar sensitivity to the electron multiplier.

Photomultiplier with conversion dynode

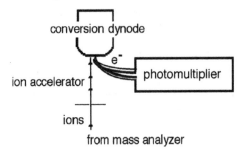

Figure 2.20. Scintillation counting with a conversion dynode and a photomultiplier relies on the conversion of the ion (or electron) signal into light. Once the photon(s) are formed, detection is performed with a photomultiplier.

Array Detector

An array detector is a group of individual detectors aligned in an array format. The array detector, which spatially detects ions according to their different m/z, has been typically used on magnetic sector mass analyzers. Spatially differentiated ions can be detected simultaneously by an array detector. The primary advantage of this approach is that, over a small mass range, scanning is not necessary and therefore sensitivity is improved.

Charge (or Inductive) Detector

Charge detectors simply recognize a moving charged particle (an ion) through the induction of a current on the plate as the ion moves past. A typical signal is shown in **Figure 2.21**. This type of detection is widely used in FTMS to generate an image current of an ion. Detection is independent of ion size and therefore has been used on particles such as whole viruses.

Charge Detection

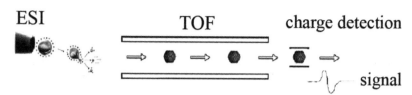

Figure 2.21. Illustration of the operation of a mass spectrometer with a charge detector; as a charged species passes through a plate it induces a current on the plate.

Table 2.3. General comparison of detectors.

Detector	Advantages	Disadvantages
Faraday Cup	Good for checking ion transmission and low sensitivity measurements	Low amplification ($\approx$10)
Photomultiplier Conversion Dynode (Scintillation Counting)	Robust Long lifetime (>5 years) Sensitive ($\approx$ gains of 10^6)	Cannot be exposed to light while in operation
Electron Multiplier	Robust Fast response Sensitive ($\approx$ gains of 10^6)	Shorter lifetime than scintillation counting (~3 years)
High Energy Dynodes with electron multiplier	Increases high mass sensitivity	May shorten lifetime of electron multiplier
Array	Fast and sensitive	Reduces resolution Expensive
Charge Detection	Detects ions independent of mass and velocity	Limited compatibility with most existing instruments

Vacuum in the Mass Spectrometer

All mass spectrometers need a vacuum to allow ions to reach the detector without colliding with other gaseous molecules or atoms. If such collisions did occur, the instrument would suffer from reduced resolution and sensitivity. Higher pressures may also cause high voltages to discharge to ground which can damage the instrument, its electronics, and/or the computer system running the mass spectrometer. An extreme leak, basically an implosion, can seriously damage a mass spectrometer by destroying electrostatic lenses, coating the optics with pump oil, and damaging the detector. In general, maintaining a good vacuum is crucial to obtaining high quality spectra.

One of the first obstacles faced by the originators of mass spectrometry was coupling the sample source to a mass spectrometer. The sample is initially at atmospheric pressure (760 torr) before being transferred into the mass spectrometer's vacuum ($\sim 10^{-6}$ torr), which represents approximately a billion-fold difference in pressure. One approach is to introduce the sample through a capillary column (GC) or through a small orifice directly into the instrument. Another approach is to evacuate the sample chamber through a vacuum lock (MALDI) and once a reasonable vacuum is achieved ($< 10^{-2}$ torr) the sample can be presented to the primary vacuum chamber ($< 10^{-5}$ torr).

A mass spectrometer is shown in **Figure 2.22** with three alternative pumping systems. All three systems are capable of producing a very high vacuum, and are all backed by a mechanical pump. The mechanical pump serves as a general workhorse for most mass spectrometers and allows for an initial vacuum of about 10^{-3} torr to be obtained. Once a 10^{-3} torr vacuum is achieved, the other pumping systems, such as diffusion, cryogenic and turbomolecular can be activated to obtain pressures as low as 10^{-11} torr.

Vacuum systems

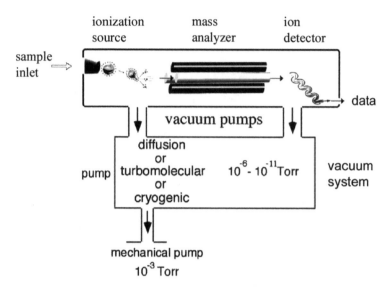

Figure 2.22. A well-maintained vacuum is essential to the function of a mass spectrometer. A couple of the different types of vacuum systems are illustrated.

Overview

The mass analyzer is a critical component to the performance of any mass spectrometer. Among the most commonly used are the quadrupole, quadrupole ion trap, time-of-flight, time-of-flight reflectron, and FTMS. However, the list is growing as more specialized analyzers allow for more difficult questions to be addressed. For example, the development of the quad-TOF has demonstrated its superior capabilities in high accuracy tandem mass spectrometry experiments. Once the ions are separated by the mass analyzer they reach the ion detector, which is ultimately responsible for the signal we observe in the mass spectrum.

Questions

- What does a mass analyzer measure?

- What is tandem mass spectrometry?

- What is a general definition of resolution?

- How does delayed extraction cool MALDI ions prior to mass analysis?

- Why is time-of-flight analysis especially well-suited to MALDI?

- What is the primary advantage of FTMS?

- Why do mass analyzers need a vacuum?

- Why are mass spectrometrists, in general, more fun?

- If you could only by one mass spectrometer, which would it be?

- Who won a Nobel prize for developing quadrupole mass analyzers?

Useful References

Busch K.L., Glish G.L., McLuckey S.A. *Mass Spectrometry/Mass Spectrometry: Techniques and Applications of Tandem.* John Wiley & Sons, **1989**.

Cotter R. *Time-Of-Flight Mass Spectrometry: Instrumentation and Applications in Biological Research.* Washington, D.C.: ACS, **1997**.

McCloskey J.A. & Simon M.I. *Methods in Enzymology: Mass Spectrometry.* Academic Press, **1997**.

Kinter M. & Sherman NE. *Protein Sequencing and Identification Using Tandem Mass Spectrometry.* Wiley-Interscience, **2000**

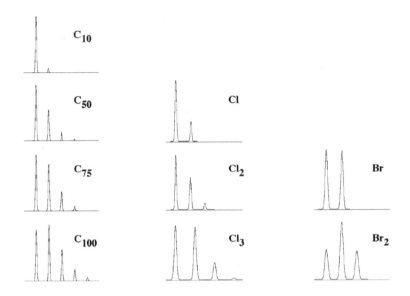

Chapter 3

Practical Aspects of Biomolecular Analysis

I know but one freedom and that is the freedom
of the mind. -Antoine de Saint-Exupery

Perspective

This chapter examines some of the practical aspects of using ESI and MALDI mass spectrometry as well as general concepts of how to make mass spectrometry experiments more successful. What is important for mass spectrometry today is in stark contrast to what was important in the past. In the 1960s and 1970s biomolecular mass analysis was typically accomplished by covalently adding protecting groups to make molecules more stable to thermal vaporization. The derivatized molecule could then be heated and vaporized into the vacuum of the mass spectrometer's ionization source. These early instruments utilized either gas phase electron excitation or chemical reactions to induce ionization. Even with derivatization (which was laborious and often required large amounts of sample), this type of mass analysis was limited to molecular weights of less than 1000 Da, but more typically less than 400 Da.

During a transition period in the early 1980s the ionization technique called fast atom/ion bombardment was developed and successfully used to analyze peptides and other biomolecules. However, FAB was found to have relatively low sensitivity and generated ions within a limited mass range. In the late 1980s ESI and MALDI dramatically improved the sensitivity of mass spectrometry and the ability to generate ions of a wide variety of biomolecules. Yet with ESI and MALDI came new considerations for preparing samples to maximize sensitivity, resolution, and accuracy.

Some important characteristics and considerations of performing mass measurements today include: Quantitation, Molecular Weight Calculation, Isotope Patterns, Ionization Characteristics, Salt Content, Sample Purity, Calibration/ Accuracy, Sensitivity, Solubility, Speed, Matrix Selection & Matrix Preparation

Quantitation

One common question about ESI and MALDI is whether the ion intensities correlate to the relative amounts of each component. In most cases MALDI does not provide this type of information unless the compound has been calibrated against an internal standard. However, for ESI it is possible to get some quantitative information based on external calibration, although internal calibration still does provide the best accuracy. **Table 3.1** lists important factors that affect the ability to perform quantitative measurements. For instance, for compounds that have similar mass and functional groups, the relative ion intensities may correspond to their content. The ability of a molecule to become ionized is closely related to its functional groups. The role of functionality in ionization is demonstrated for two compounds, an amine and an amide in **Figure 3.1**. Both are at the same concentration yet they have significantly different signals because of the relatively high proton affinity of the amine. Another example is shown in **Figure 3.2** where excellent linearity is obtained between very similar compounds, the cyclic peptides cyclosporine A and G, because they differ only by a methylene group. Generally speaking, the best quantitation is obtained when a compound is calibrated against an internal standard similar to the molecule in question.

Table 3.1. Factors affecting quantitation.

Averaging	The signal to noise ratio (S/N) is directly proportional to the square root of the number of scans averaged. More averaging results in less errors associated with random noise.

$$S/N \propto N^{1/2}$$

Amount of material	Signal intensity will fluctuate significantly at low sample amounts, reducing quantitative capability. MALDI typically provides a less stable signal than ESI and therefore generates bigger errors with less sample. Picomole quantities of material will generally provide good quantitation and with some instrumentation it is possible to go down to the low femtomole level.
Dynamic signal range	Analyzers, such as quadrupole ion traps, have a relatively small dynamic range ($\sim 10^3$-10^4) and can easily get saturated. Quadrupole analyzers have a larger dynamic signal range ($\sim 10^6$) and are therefore more well suited to quantitative measurements.
Ionization technique (instrument stability)	ESI has a relatively stable signal and as a result excellent quantitation can be achieved with a minimal amount of averaging. MALDI is less stable (from laser shot to laser shot) and requires greater care in obtaining the quantitative data.
Compound's functional groups	The functional groups on a molecule can drastically affect the ionization properties. For instance, an amine will pick up a proton far more efficiently than an amide. Therefore in order to obtain good quantitative data an internal standard with comparable ionization characteristics is desirable.
Choice of internal standard	An internal standard with comparable ionization characteristics to the compound of interest allows for consistent relative signal stability. The best choice is an isotopically labeled internal standard.
Consistent sample handling	Variations in sampling handling approaches (solvents, mixing, injecting...) can have a significant effect on the quality of quantitative results.

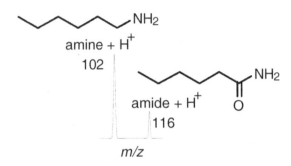

Figure 3.1. The ESI mass spectrum was obtained from an equal amount of each compound, illustrating that the ion intensity does not necessarily correlate to the amount of sample being analyzed.

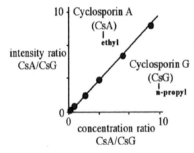

Figure 3.2. The quantitative analysis of cyclosporin A using cyclosporin G as an internal standard. These two molecules differ by a single methylene group which makes their ionization properties, for practical purposes, very similar. Cyclosporin G (0.20 µM) was used as an internal standard. Similar results were obtained with ESI and MALDI-MS.

Calculating Molecular Weight

There are three different ways to calculate mass from the molecular formula: the average mass, the monoisotopic mass, and the nominal mass. Each calculation is used for specific reasons; for instance average mass calculation is used when the individual isotopes are not distinguishable (**Figure 3.3**, resolution = 200). The monoisotopic mass is calculated when it is possible to distinguish the isotopes (**Figure 3.3**, resolution = 2000). The nominal mass is not often used, yet is typically applied to compounds containing the elements C, H, N, O and S and having a mass below 600 Da. Examples are shown in **Table 3.2**.

Monoisotopic mass (exact mass) -- The mass of an ion for a given empirical formula calculated using the *exact* mass of the most abundant isotope of each element.

Average mass -- The mass of an ion for a given empirical formula, calculated using the average atomic weight averaged over all the isotopes for each element.

Nominal mass -- The mass of an ion with a given empirical formula calculated using the *integer* mass of the most abundant isotope of each element.

A compound with a formula $C_{60}H_{122}N_{20}O_{16}S_2$ has a monoisotopic mass of 1442.8788, an average mass of 1443.8857 and a nominal mass of 1442. It should be noted that the calculation of the protonated species is the addition of a proton (1.0073) and not a hydrogen (1.0078), this makes a significant difference with high accuracy instruments.

Table 3.2. An illustration of the differences between monoisotopic, average, and nominal mass for some elements, a lipid, a sugar, and a peptide.

Name	Molecular Formula	Monoisotopic Mass (Da)	Average Mass (Da)	Nominal Mass (Da)
Hydrogen	H	1.0078	1.0080	1
Proton	H^+	1.0073	1.0075	1
Carbon	C	12.0000	12.0112	12
Nitrogen	N	14.0031	14.0067	14
Oxygen	O	15.9949	15.9994	16
Sulfur	S	31.9721	32.0600	32
A lipid	$C_{18}H_{35}N_{101}$	281.2718	281.4858	281
A sugar	$C_{56}H_{118}N_4O_{14}$	1070.8644	1071.5833	1070
A peptide	$C_{101}H_{258}N_{24}O_{24}$	2191.9704	2193.3288	2190

One of the most important features of a mass spectrometer is resolving power (Chapter 2) which turns out to also be important when calculating the mass of a molecule. For example if the isotopes can be distinguished in the mass spectrum, the observed *m/z* will correspond to the monoisotopic mass. This is illustrated in **Figure 3.3** where at a resolution of 2000 on an electrospray quadrupole instrument there is sufficient resolving power to distinguish isotopes on a peptide. FTMS instruments, because of their high resolving power, can provide isotopic distributions of proteins with mass above 10,000 Da. Generally speaking, the average mass is a satisfactory calculation for compounds above a mass of 5000 Da while for compounds below 5000 Da, the resolution of the instrument is an important factor in determining which mass calculation to use.

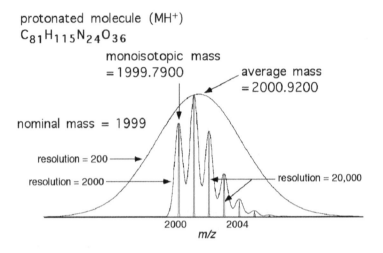

protonated molecule (MH$^+$)
$C_{81}H_{115}N_{24}O_{36}$

monoisotopic mass = 1999.7900

average mass = 2000.9200

nominal mass = 1999

resolution = 200

resolution = 2000

resolution = 20,000

2000   2004
m/z

Figure 3.3. The mass spectrum of a protonated molecule obtained at resolving powers of 200, 2000, and 20,000 (using the FWHM definition of resolution). This is an example of how the resolving power can have a dramatic effect on resolving isotopes.

Isotope Patterns

Figure 3.3 illustrates how the isotope pattern of an individual molecule, as well as the resolving power of the mass spectrometer, can effect the mass spectrum. A mass spectrometer with a resolving power of 2000 can resolve the isotopes for ions of at least 2000 Da. **Figure 3.3** also demonstrates the effect isotopes can have on the observed molecular weight. Compounds containing ^{12}C, ^{1}H, ^{14}N, and ^{16}O have isotopes ^{13}C, ^{2}H, ^{15}N, ^{17}O, and ^{18}O in relatively low abundance (1.10%, 0.015%, 0.366%, 0.038%, and 0.200%, respectively) yet these less abundant isotopes make a significant contribution when enough atoms are present.

The isotope patterns are often taken for granted, but they can be a great source of information. For instance, the spacing of the isotopes can tell you about the charge state (e.g. 1/2 spacing = 2^+ charge state, 1/3 spacing = 3^+ charge state). In addition, certain elements have distinct isotope patterns such as chlorine and bromine. Looking at the isotopic patterns in **Figure 3.4**, note that a compound containing one chlorine atom will have an isotopic contribution that correlates to a peak having a mass at **M + 2** , with a height of ~32% of the primary ion. The percentage contribution for chlorine and bromine will change if more of these halogens are added to the compound. Observing these isotopes can be a useful confirmation of the presence of these elements.

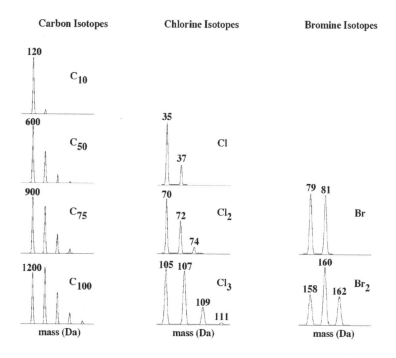

Figure 3.4. The isotope patterns associated with carbon, chlorine and bromine. The chlorine and bromine isotopes produce characteristic patterns that help one readily identify these elements in a compound. For carbon the natural contribution of 1.1% of the 13C accounts for the isotopic abundance of 13C at higher numbers of carbons.

Below 3000 Da the most common isotopic distribution that you will observe for biological compounds is dominated by carbon (**Figure 3.4**) since less abundant isotopes of hydrogen, oxygen, and nitrogen do not significantly contribute to the distribution below this mass. However sulfurs can present a significant contribution as 34S is abundant at 4.68%.

Solubility

Sample solubility is absolutely critical to obtaining quality data. For instance, if you are performing ESI on a sample that has precipitated out of solvent, you will not observe that compound. The solvent or matrix is the medium that allows your sample to be transported to the gas phase. Moreover, solvent often plays an important role in ionization. For techniques like ESI and APCI, if your compound is not soluble in the solvent, it will be impossible to observe a signal. **Figure 3.5** illustrates the dramatic effect that choosing a suitable solvent can have on acquiring data.

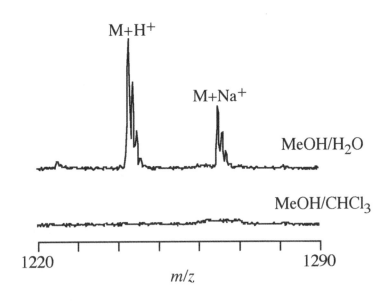

Figure 3.5. Electrospray mass spectra of a peptide analyzed from methanol/water (top) and in methanol/chloroform (bottom). In this example the peptide was not observed in the methanol/chloroform solvent system.

Timing

Analyzing the sample as soon as possible after it has been prepared is important, as it is quite common for compounds to decompose or even react with the solvent in a relatively short time. A problem associated with hydrophobic compounds is loss of the sample to the container's surface. Another phenomenon that has been observed is that a sample solution may even leech some salts or plasticizers from the container.

Calibration/Accuracy

Accuracy is one of the most important aspects of the data obtained from a mass spectrometer. It is important for compound identification and more recently, for high accuracy measurement of proteolytic peptide fragments for protein identification. In order for high accuracy to be possible one needs an instrument with resolution on the order of ~4000 or higher. For very high accuracy (< 5 ppm) it is often necessary to have an internal standard present or at least some reference compound. Standard compounds are used to calibrate a mass spectrometer's mass analyzer with respect to how it measures the *m/z* (**Figure 3.6**). Standards are also used internally (**Figure 3.7**) while running an unknown sample to improve accuracy. Calibration is generally performed using a standard mixture that generates a reliable source of known ions that cover the mass range of interest. For instance, polypropylene glycols (PPG's) have been used as electrospray calibrants. To remove the ambiguity associated with the isotope peaks generated with polypropylene glycols, cesium iodide (CsI) has also been used for calibration (**Figure 3.6**) or fluorinated phosphonium salts. Flourinated compounds are useful because monoisotopic fluorine minimizes the isotope contribution and therefore make the signals simple to interpret. When a calibration compound of known mass is measured, it helps determine whether the instrument is running within acceptable error limits. If the instrument is off in accuracy, an adjustment based on the calibration compound will allow the instrument to run accurately again.

It is important to distinguish between internal and external calibration. External calibration refers to the instrument being calibrated followed by analysis without the presence of a calibrant. Internal calibration refers to analyses that are performed with a calibrant present to improve accuracy. "Acceptable" levels of accuracy are highly dependent on the mass analyzer; for a quadrupole ~200 ppm is acceptable; for FTMS ~5 ppm is acceptable with external calibration. Internal calibration, ~100 ppm for quadrupoles and <5 ppm for FTMS is acceptable. Interestingly, TOF mass analyzers have recently been improved to obtain <5 ppm with internal calibration. The improvements to TOF analyzers include making the flight tube from material that has a low thermal expansion coefficient (the flight tube does not change appreciably as a function of temperature) and improved detector response time.

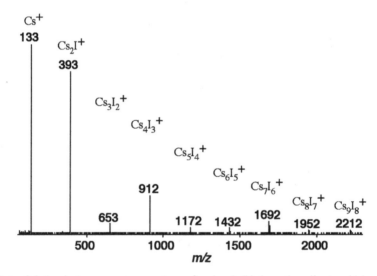

Figure 3.6. An electrospray mass spectrum of cesium iodide in methanol/water which was used for calibration.

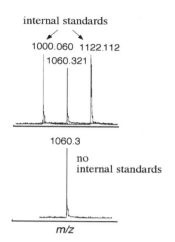

Figure 3.7. The internal standards can be used to obtain high accuracy when used with high resolution instruments. In this case the spectral data containing the internal standards allows us to get accuracy to the 5 ppm level or better.

The calibration of MALDI TOF and ESI quadrupole mass spectrometers often uses the standard mixtures shown in **Table 3.3**.

Table 3.3. Common MALDI and ESI calibration compounds and their mass-to-charge (*m/z*) ratios.

Calibrants	MH$^+$	MH$_2^{2+}$	MH$_3^{3+}$
Matrix-Assisted Laser Desorption/Ionization (MALDI) Calibrants			
Angiotensin II	1046.54 (mono*)		
	1047.20 (avg)**		
ACTH (18-39)	2465.20 (mono)		
	2466.73 (avg)		
Insulin bovine	5734.56 (avg)	2867.78 (avg)	
apo-Myoglobin equine	16952.47 (avg)	8476.74 (avg)	
Cytochrome C equine	12,361.09 (avg)	6181.05 (avg)	
BSA	66,430 (avg)	33216 (avg)	22144. (avg)
BSA-dimer	132,859 (avg)	66430 (avg)	44287. (avg)
Electrospray Ionization (ESI) Calibrants			
PPG	100-3000 *m/z*		
CsI	100-3000 *m/z*		
Agilent calibrant ($C_xH_yO_zN_aP_bF_c$)	100-3000 *m/z*		

*mono is monoisotopic mass
**avg is average mass

Sample Purity and Clean Containers

Whether analysis is being performed with MALDI or ESI, sample purity maximizes sensitivity. It is true that salts can facilitate ionization for certain compounds such as carbohydrates, however, in general, excessive salt and other contaminants will lead to reduced sensitivity. An effective approach for higher sensitivity ESI-MS is reverse phase liquid chromatography since separates compounds prior to analysis. Two common methods (**Figure 3.8**) of cleaning samples for MALDI-MS analysis involve **ZipTip**^{TM} or cold water washing, both of which are effective for salt removal.

Figure 3.8.

ZipTip^{TM} pipette tip containing C18 material

- ZipTip^{TM} is placed on standard pipetter;
- sample is aspirated onto the C18 material;
- is washed and eluted.

On-plate MALDI wash

- add 1µl of sample to plate and allow to dry;
- add matrix;
- allow to dry;
- add 4µl of H_2O, allow to sit for 10 seconds, remove.

Generally, the more pure or homogenous a compound is, the better the sensitivity and quality of the mass spectral data. For example, electrospray requires that the sample be relatively free (less than 10 millimolar concentration) of salts, buffers, and other contaminants because these impurities have a detrimental effect on the electrosprayed droplets and their ability to evaporate. If a droplet cannot effectively evaporate because of reduced vapor pressure associated with impurities, ion production will be lost. Another effect of contamination is the loss of sensitivity due to the contaminants' competition for protons/cations in the droplets. Using liquid chromatography as a sample introduction method for ESI-MS is very effective for generating pure sample and therefore maximizing signal.

Even though MALDI is known to be more tolerant of salts, buffers, and impurities, cleanup procedures are still useful. With MALDI, one typically probes the surface with the laser beam until a reasonable signal has been found. A good signal is generated as a result of the laser beam striking a portion of the probe that has the sample embedded in crystalline matrix. To facilitate sample incorporation and desalting, the sample can be washed clean using a droplet of cold water (**Figure 3.8**). This method promotes a greater and more uniform ion signal.

Table 3.4 presents an overview of the effect different salts and detergents can have on ESI and MALDI. Tris-HCl (25-50mM) and ammonium bicarbonate (25-50 mM) are considered the most compatible buffers with mass spectrometry. Conveniently, these buffers are also compatible with enzymes such as Arg-C, Trp, Lys-C, Chymo, and Glu-C.

It can go without saying that containers such as glass or eppendorfs should be clean, however sample containers cleanliness can vary widely from manufacturer to manufacturer. So it is another source of potential contamination to consider when problem solving.

Table 3.4. Maximum surfactant & buffer concentrations for MALDI & ESI.

Surfactant, Buffer & Salts	MW (g/mol)	MALDI (mM)	MALDI (wt.%)	ESI (mM)	ESI (wt.%)	Reference
TRIS	121	100	1.0	n. a.	n. a.	A, B
HEPES	238	100	2.4	n. a.	n. a.	A, B
BICINE	163	50	0.8	n. a.	n. a.	B
Urea	60	500	3.0	n. a.	n. a.	C, D
Guanidine, HCl	96	250	2.4	n. a.	n. a.	C, D
Dithiothreitol	154	500	7.7	n. a.	n. a.	D
Glycerol	92	130	1.2	n. a.	n. a.	C, D
N-Octyl-ᴅ-glucopyranoside	292	3.4	0.1	3.4	0.1	C, E
n-Octyl sucrose	468	n. a.	n. a.	2.1	0.1	E
n-Dodecyl sucrose	524	n. a.	n. a.	1.9	0.1	E
n-Dodecyl maltoside	511	n. a.	n. a.	2.0	0.1	E
Octyl thioglucoside	308	n. a.	n. a.	3.2	0.1	E
n- Hexyl glucoside	264	n. a.	n. a.	3.8	0.1	E
n-Dodecyl glucoside	348	n. a.	n. a.	2.9	0.1	E
PEG1000	1000	n. a.	n. a.	0.5	0.05	F
PEG2000	2000	0.5	0.1	n. a.	n. a.	C,
Triton X-100	628	1.6	0.1	<1.6	<0.1	C, E
NP-40	603	1.7	0.1	n.a.	n. a.	
Zwittergent, 3-16	392	2.6	0.1	n. a.	n. a.	C
Tween20	1228	n. a.	n. a.	0.81	0.1	E
Thesit	583	n. a.	n. a.	<1.7	<0.1	E
SDS	288	0.35	0.01	0.335	0.01	C, D, E, F
LDAO	229	4.4	1.0	<4.4	<0.1	C, F
CTAB	284	n. a.	n. a.	<3.5	<0.1	F
CHAPS	615	0.16	0.01	1.6	0.1	C, E
Sodium Cholate	431	n. a.	n. a.	2.3	0.1	E
Sodium Taurocholate	538	n. a.	n. a.	<1.9	<0.1	F
Sodium Azide	65	15	0.1	3.1	0.02	C, F
NH$_4$HCO$_3$	79	50	0.4	n. a.	n. a.	D
NaCl	58	50	0.29	n. a.	n. a.	C, D
Sodium Acetate	82	50	0.41	n. a.	n. a.	B, C
NaHPO$_4$	120	10	0.12	10	0.12	B, C, D, F
TFA	114	n. a.	n. a.	4.4	0.05	Pri. Comm.

*Note: With multiple recommendations the lowest concentration was chosen.

HEPES: N-[2-hydroxyethyl]piperazine-N'-[2-ethanesulfonic acid]
TRIS: Tris[hydroxymethyl]aminomethane acetate
BICINE: N,N-bis[2-hydroxyethyl]glycine
TFA: Trifluoroacetic acid
CHAPS: 3-[(3-cholamidopropyl)-dimethylammonio]-1-propane sulfonate
PEG: polyethylene glycol
LDAO: Lauryldimethylamine oxide

References:

A: Kallweit U. et al., Rapid Comm. Mass Spec. 10, 845-849, 1996.
B: Yao J. et al., J. Am. Soc. Mass Spectrom 9, 805-813, 1998.
C: Coligan J. E. et al., In Current Protocols in Protein Science 2, 16.2.
D: Gevaert K. et al., ABRF web publication, 1998.
E: Ogorzalek et al., Protein Science 3, 1975-1983.
F. Kay I. and Mallet A. I. Rapid Comm. Mass Spec. 7 , 744-746, 1993.

Sensitivity / Saturation

Too little or even too much sample will have a dramatic effect on the data and can make the difference between a successful and an unsuccessful analysis. For example, if too little sample is used, understandably the instrument will be unable to detect a signal. If too much is used it can skew the intensity profile of the ions observed (**Figure 3.9**). High concentrations can also make impurities appear to be more dominant or even cause signal suppression. An important point is that higher concentration is not always better and that it is more important to be within the correct range for your instrument.

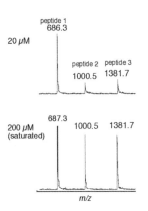

Figure 3.9. The electrospray mass spectra of three peptides is shown. At 20 µM concentration of peptide 1 the two other peptides can be observed. However, at a 10-fold higher concentration (200 µM) the relatively minor impurities, peptides 2 and 3, now appear as major components due to detector saturation of peptide 1. Peptide 1 is so saturated that the C13 isotope of this peptide appears to be bigger than the 12C.

But what is the "right" range? The answer is highly dependent on the instrument, sample, and technique. Some instruments of very similar design can vary widely in terms of their dynamic range. However, **Table 3.5** provides some general guidelines for the amount of sample required according to the ionization technique. **Table 3.5** converts a range of concentrations often used in electrospray and MALDI from micromolar (20-50 µM) to milligrams/milliliter with respect to molecular weight. Those used for FAB analysis are also displayed. The concentrations shown are conservative; most instruments will easily handle significantly lower concentrations. In general, however, the concentrations listed will produce good signal even in the presence of some salt or other contaminating compounds. In comparing ESI, MALDI, and FAB, **Table 3.5** illustrates the improvements that ESI and MALDI offer and why they are so important today.

Table 3.5. Typical concentration range for ESI and MALDI (with conversion to µg/µl) as it compares to traditional FAB technology.

Molecular Weight	MALDI or ESI (1 nanomolar to 50 micromolar)	FAB (1 millimolar)
500 Da	0.0000005 - 0.025 µg/µL	≥ 0.50 µg/µL
1000 Da	0.000001 - 0.05 µg/µL	≥ 1.00 µg/µL
5000 Da	0.000005 - 0.25 µg/µL	≥ 5.00 µg/µL
10,000 Da	0.00001 - 0.50 µg/µL	≥10.00 µg/µL
50,000 Da	0.00005 - 2.50 µg/µL	not applicable
100,000 Da	0.0001 - 5.00 µg/µL	not applicable

* Typical sample volumes used for MALDI, ESI & FAB are 1, 10, and 2µL, respectively.

Ionization Characteristics

The types of functional groups on a molecule will often determine how a compound should be analyzed. When analyzing a compound by ESI or MALDI, first look for sites on the molecule that can be ionized. Amines (+), acids (-), and amides (+) represent easily ionizable functional groups, while hydroxyl groups, esters, ketones, and aldehydes do not accept a charge as easily and are therefore more difficult to ionize, typically resulting in weak ion signals. Due to the presence of amide and amine groups, peptides usually ionize easily through protonation. Because peptides often contain amino acid residues with side chain carboxyl groups, they can also be observed in the negative ion mode by deprotonation. Some carbohydrates will accept a proton because of the presence of an amide bond, but in general they form stable ions upon the addition of a cation other than a proton, such as Na^+ or K^+ to form $M + Na^+$ and $M + K^+$ ions. Oligonucleotides, proteins, and the myriad of small molecules each have their ionization peculiarities, making the conditions under which analysis is performed all the more important.

Table 3.6 describes some of the different ways different compounds are analyzed.

Table 3.6. Typical ionization properties for biomolecules.

Compound	Ionization Mechanism	MALDI & ESI Ionization
Peptides	Protonation/Deprotonation	Positive/Negative
Proteins	Protonation	Positive
Membrane Proteins	Protonation	Positive
Glycoproteins	Protonation	Positive
Carbohydrates & Protected Carbohydrates	Protonation/Cationization/Deprotonation Anionization	Positive/Negative
Oligonucleotides	Protonation/ Deprotonation	Positive/Negative
Protected Oligonucleotides	Deprotonation/Protonation/Cationization	Positive/Negative
Small Biomolecules	Protonation/Cationization/Deprotonation Anionization Electron Ejection Electron Capture	Positive/Negative

Matrix Selection/Preparation

The choice of matrix is critical for mass analysis and, in many cases, will determine the quality of the data (**Figure 3.10**). Matrix selection and preparation for MALDI-MS was initially very simple; however, the introduction of new matrix recipes has complicated matrix selection, and at the same time had a tremendous impact on sensitivity and accuracy. For instance, because of these new matricies, it is becoming more common to observe peptides with attomole sensitivity or lower (Chapter 4).

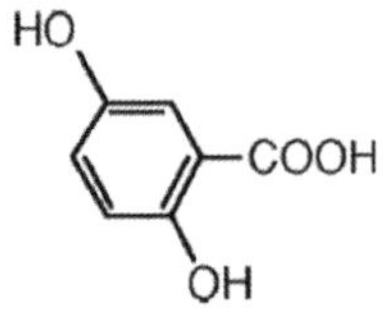

2,5-dihydroxy benzoic acid (DHB)
peptides, carbohydrates, synthetic
polymers, and glycolipids

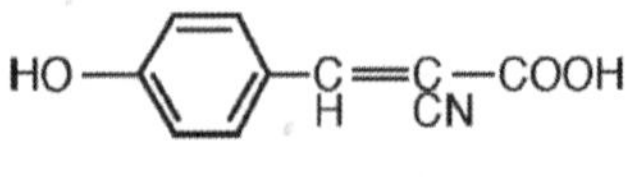

α-cyano-4-hydroxycinnamic acid
(CCA)
peptides and proteins

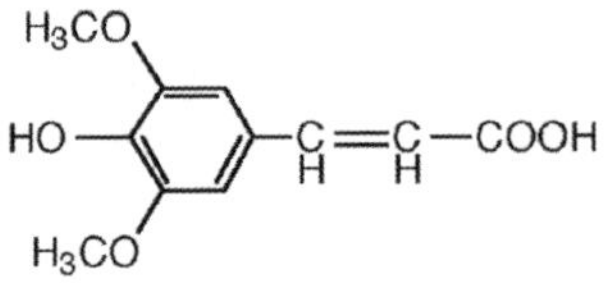

3,5-dimethoxy-4-hydroxycinnamic acid
(sinapinic acid) peptides and proteins

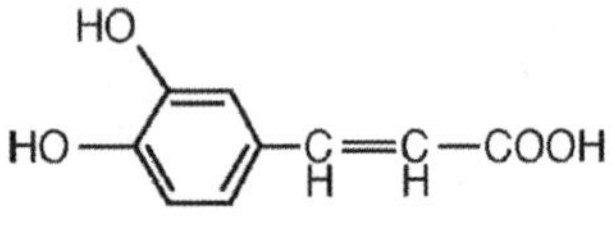

3,4-dihydroxycinnamic acid (ferulic
acid)
peptides, proteins, and some oligos

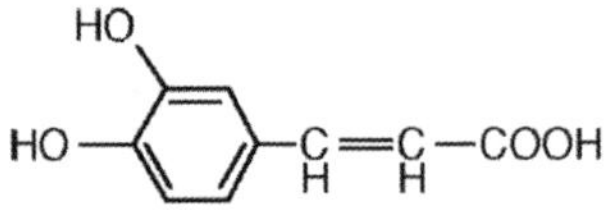

3,4-dihydroxycinnamic acid (caffeic
acid)
peptides, proteins, and some oligos

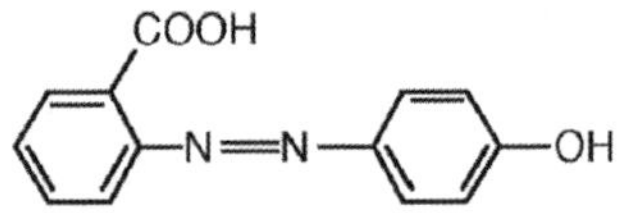

2-(4-hydroxyphenylazo)-benzoic acid
(caffeic acid) (HABA)
large proteins, polar and nonpolar
synthetic polymers

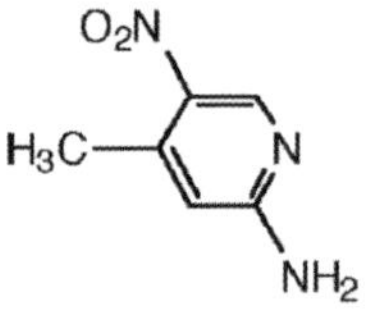

2-amino-4-methyl-5-nitropyridine
small acid-sensitive proteins (<12,000
Da)

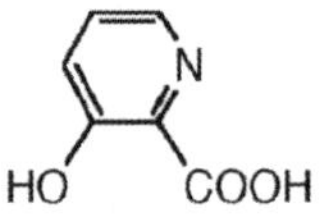

3-hydroxypicolinic acid (HPA) with
ammoniumn citrate additive
oligonucleotides

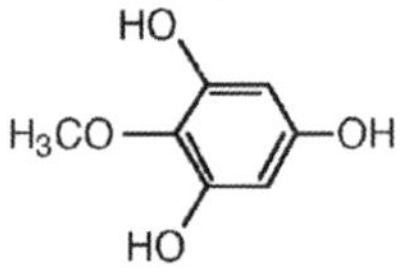

2,4,6-trihydroxy acetophonone (THAP)
with ammoniumn citrate additive
oligonucleotides

Figure 3.10. Cinnamic acid is the basis of many of the common MALDI matricies. Sample deposition involves placing the sample and matrix onto a probe at a ratio of roughly 10,000 matrix molecules to every sample molecule. The type of matrix is important with regards to the type of compound being analyzed.

Sample preparation with MALDI involves dissolving the sample into a solvent, such as water, acetone, or methanol. The sample solution is then added to the matrix, commonly a nicotinic acid or cinnamic acid derivative, at a ratio of approximately 1 part sample to 10,000 parts matrix. Approximately 10 picomoles (1 μl of a 10 μM solution) of the sample is added to an equal volume of a saturated solution of the matrix. It is important to note that MALDI most commonly involves a solid matrix and, therefore, MALDI sample preparation requires that after the sample solution is made up and deposited upon the probe, it is necessary to wait a few minutes for complete evaporation of the solvent to leave a solid mixture of the sample embedded in the matrix.

Because a sample cannot be analyzed until the solvent completely evaporates, sample preparation for MALDI will usually take longer than FAB preparation. The evaporation process can be expedited by flowing a stream of nitrogen or air over the dissolved matrix or by using a volatile solvent (acetone) if possible. Multisample probes also quicken the analysis time by allowing for many samples to be prepared at once.

Overview

This chapter examines many of the factors that allow for quality mass spectral information from ESI and MALDI mass spectrometers. Among the most important of these factors for obtaining signal of high quality is sample solubility, matrix selection, the ionization characteristics, salt content and purity. Factors that contribute to data interpretation include the isotope patterns, saturation effects and accuracy.

Common Questions

Question	Answer
1) What concentration of material do you need to perform a routine mass measurement?	~1-50 µM for electrospray ~1-50 µM for MALDI ~1000 µM for FAB
2) If you have the appropriate concentration what volume of solution do you need?	~10 µl for electrospray ~1 µl for nanoelectrospray ~1 µl for MALDI ~1 µl for FAB
3) In a typical mass spectrometry experiment what would be the maximum mass range expected from each instrument?	~70,000 Da by electrospray ~300,000 Da by MALDI ~7000 Da by FAB
4) What does resolving power mean in mass spectrometry?	Resolving power is the ability of a mass spectrometer to separate ions of similar mass-to-charge ratio (m/z). High resolution enables the analyst to resolve isotopic peaks of high-mass ions. Most commonly, resolving power is defined as $M/\Delta M$ as shown below and **Figure 3.3**.

protonated molecule (MH^+)
$C_{81}H_{115}N_{24}O_{36}$

monoisotopic mass = 1999.7905

average mass = 2000.9200

nominal mass = 1999

resolution = 200

resolution = 2000

resolution = 20,000

m/z

Resolving power = $M/\Delta M$ = 500/.5 = 1000

Resolving power = $M/\Delta M$ = 500/.5 = 1000

5) Are there always matrix peaks in the MALDI mass spectra?	Most often below m/z 500. It is possible for certain analytes to adjust the analyte-to-matrix ratio to minimize the matrix interference effect.
6) Do you observe matrix peaks with electrospray?	No. Since electrospray does not use a matrix, it does not generate matrix peaks. However it does use solvents like water, methanol, and acetonitrile and it is possible to observe aggregates of these. At high salt concentrations it is also possible to see salt clusters and the observation of nonspecific noncovalent interactions with electrospray is quite common.

Question	Answer
7) Why are cation adducts predominantly observed in the mass spectrum of some molecules?	Some compounds do not form stable protonated molecules because the charge from the proton can be transferred onto the molecule and can thus destabilize it. Alkali cations can complex to some molecules because the charge remains localized and does not transfer onto the molecule (there is no charge destabilization). Therefore, the alkali cation adducts of some molecules are more readily observed than the protonated species.
8) How can you tell if a peak in electrospray is singly- or multiply- charged?	The spacing in isotope pattern will tell you what the charge state is. For instance, if the isotopes are spaced one m/z apart, the peak corresponds to a singly charged ion. If the isotopes are one half m/z apart then the peak corresponds to a doubly charged ion. If the peaks isotopes are spaced one third of a m/z apart then the peak corresponds to a triply charged ion. And so on. Most instruments do not have the resolving power to resolve more than the triply charged isotopic patterns.
9) Electron ionization used to be the most popular ionization source, why is it not used as much anymore?	Electron ionization requires thermal desorption in order to vaporize a compound and many compounds will not survive the high temperature to get them into the gas phase. Also, the electron ionization process is a relatively harsh ionization process and many molecules will not remain intact once ionized in this way.
10) Why does having too much salt in your electrospray sample cause signal suppression?	Electrospray ionization operates by the evaporation of charged droplets. Too much salt causes vapor pressure to go down and evaporation is thus inhibited.
11) Why do heterogeneous mixtures reduce the sensitivity of MALDI and electrospray?	MALDI and electrospray are both somewhat competitive ionization techniques in the sense that molecules in solution or the matrix will compete for protons. Therefore, the compound with the highest proton affinity will often dominate the spectrum. This tends to be more the case for electrospray since the molecules are competing in solution, while for MALDI many of the molecules are separated in the matrix solution, therefore reducing competition.
12) How should volatile samples be analyzed?	Volatile samples typically require more traditional ionization sources such as electron ionization.
13) How important is it to know the structure of a compound when performing mass analysis?	Structural information can be useful since it helps the analyst decide how to perform the analysis. For example, an acidic compound would be analyzed in negative ionization mode.

3. Practical Aspects of Biomolecular Analysis

Question	Answer
14) Why is it so important that you do not obtain fragmentation during ionization with ESI and MALDI?	The problem with obtaining fragment ions is that you can never be sure that the largest ion that is observed is really the molecular ion and not a fragment of something bigger. This is why ESI and MALDI are so useful; in almost all cases the ion generated corresponds to the intact molecular ion.

Chapter 4
Peptide and Protein Analysis
"This is the sum of our ambition." -Sting

Perspective

This chapter describes how mass spectrometry is being used for peptide and protein characterization, focusing on the application of electrospray ionization (ESI) and matrix-assisted laser desorption/ionization (MALDI) to determine molecular weight.

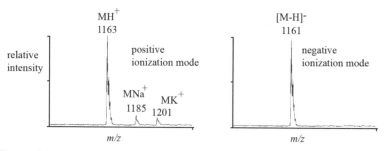

Figure 4.1. Electrospray ionization mass spectra of a peptide in positive and negative ionization modes.

Overview of Peptide and Protein Analysis

What has made the mass analysis of peptides and proteins possible is the ability to promote their nondestructive vaporization/ionization through either ESI or MALDI. Ionization for these methods occurs through the addition or removal of protons such as $[M + H]^+$, $[M + 2H]^{2+}$, $[M + nH]^{n+}$, or $[M - nH]^{n-}$ (**Figure 4.1**). During the generation of these species it is fortunate that little to no fragmentation is observed by either ESI or MALDI for peptides and virtually no fragmentation is observed for proteins. As a result, the generation of molecular weight information is unambiguous.

In general, the sensitivity of mass spectrometry is quite good for proteins and peptides. It is possible to observe peptides at the attomole level, while the sensitivity for protein analysis is typically lower because of the protein's larger size. Proteins strike the detector with lower velocity than smaller molecules, resulting in less signal output. Even so, the sensitivity of MALDI and ESI for proteins is still considered good at the picomole to femtomole level.

In addition to molecular weight determination (**Figure 4.2**), MALDI and ESI have demonstrated increasing utility in the identification of proteins and protein post-translational modifications. While complete and routine sequence determination through mass analysis of proteins is yet to be realized, it is now possible to use proteolytic peptide fragments in combination with database searching algorithms to identify proteins. This is accomplished by combining mass spectrometry with enzymatic or chemical digestion (**Figure 4.2 insert**) followed by mass analysis of the peptide products and database searching techniques (especially useful in the post genome age).

Mass spectrometry has also demonstrated its utility in identifying post-translational modifications, as these modifications usually lead to a predictable change in molecular weight. In addition, electrospray with tandem mass spectrometry is demonstrating a capacity for performing de novo sequencing. This chapter as well as Chapter 5 focuses on the current analysis capabilities in peptide and protein mass spectrometry, some specific preparation procedures, matrix selection, and the application of MALDI and ESI for protein identification and post-translational modification characterization.

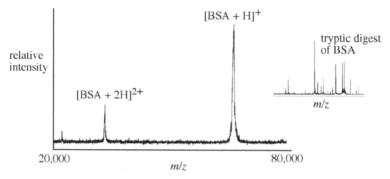

Figure 4.2. A typical MALDI mass spectrum of the protein bovine serum albumin (BSA) with inset of the tryptic digest of BSA.

Peptides and Proteins by MALDI

MALDI is useful for peptide and protein analysis for the following reasons:

- MALDI allows for rapid sample analysis (using multi-sample plates, **Figure 4.3**)

- high sensitivity (in the femtomole range or better)

- tolerance of heterogeneous samples such as proteolytic digests (**Figures 4.2 & 4.4**)

- typically high accuracy mass measurements can now be generated on a MALDI-TOF reflectron in the mass range below 3000 m/z or higher with a MALDI FTMS

- good dynamic range (**Figure 4.5**)

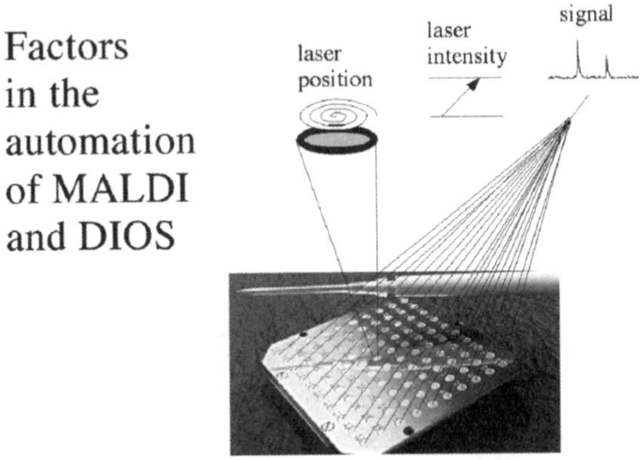

Factors in the automation of MALDI and DIOS

Figure 4.3. MALDI can employ multisample preparation and automated sample analysis. Three different parameters can be used to adjust and monitor autosampling, including laser position, laser intensity, and signal intensity.

Surface-based ionization techniques like MALDI and DIOS allow for rapid analyses primarily because both allow for the preparation of multiple samples simultaneously through the use of multi-sample probes. The automation of those analyses is becoming increasingly important in proteomics and combinatorial chemistry. These analyses are driven by a computer-controlled procedure to monitor the ion signal as a function of laser position and laser intensity (**Figure 4.3**). To accomplish this, the computer workstation automatically adjusts laser intensity and searches the sample well until a signal (within the specified mass range and intensity threshold) is obtained. Based on a careful preselection of autosampler options, each parameter (laser intensity, search pattern, step size in well, signal intensity, and m/z range) is adjusted to minimize time of analysis and maximize signal quality.

For MALDI analysis of relatively small molecules and peptides (400 Da - 1000 Da), 2,5-dihydroxybenzoic acid (DHB) matrix produces less interference than other matrices. Matrices such as α-cyano-4-hydroxycinnamic acid (α-cyano) give a high matrix background although they are particularly good for generating ions above 700 Daltons. For peptides generated by enzymatic digestion, α-cyano is often the matrix of choice. 3,5-dimethoxy-4-

hydroxycinnamic acid (sinapinic acid), another common matrix, is most commonly used for whole protein analysis. Most matrices reported to date have been acidic, but basic matrices have also been introduced, such as 2-amino-4-methyl-5-nitropyridine and trihydroxyacetophenone (THAP), which extends the utility of MALDI to acid-sensitive peptides, proteins, or other acid-sensitive compounds. Interestingly, different matrices can provide dramatically different results on the same sample (**Figure 4.4**).

MALDI Sample Preparation Procedures

Whole proteins

- A saturated solution of sinapinic acid can be prepared in acetonitrile, water and TFA (50/50 acetonitrile/water with 0.1% TFA) or acetonitrile/water/TFA=1:1:0.1 and vortexed for complete mixing. The solution is ready for use when the undissolved solid settles.

- Place 0.5 μL protein solution (1-10 pmol/μL) directly on plate and then add 0.5 μL matrix solution.

- Perform on-plate wash with 2 μL nanopure H_2O when sample is salty or buffers were used.

Protein digests

- Typical in-solution digest ratios are 1:20 – 1:50 (enzyme weight : protein weight).

- Digestion conditions include mixing 2.5 μL of 1 mg/mL denatured protein with 4 μL trypsin (0.1 mg/mL), 7.5 μL 200 mM NH_4HCO_3 buffer, and 6 μL H_2O allowing to digest at 37° C overnight.

- In preparation for MALDI analysis, deposit 0.5 μL of proteoltyic peptide solution (~1 pmol/μL) on plate and then immediately add 0.5 μL matrix solution.

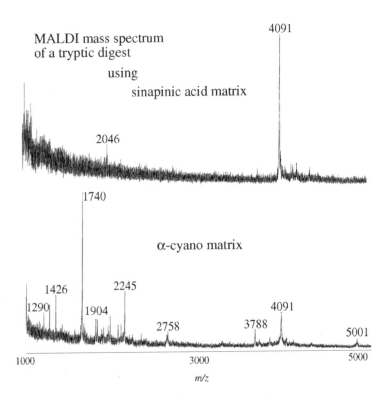

Figure 4.4. MALDI-MS analyses of the same tryptic digest of a protein using sinapinic acid and α-cyano matrices. Different matrices can provide significantly different MALDI results on the same sample.

Using the dried droplet method of sample crystallization, 0.1 to 1.0 picomole are introduced onto a MALDI plate, after which an equal amount of matrix solution is added to the sample. The mixture is then set to dry at room temperature or placement in a 37 °C incubator can assist sample drying. Washing the dried sample/matrix with cold water can serve to remove contaminants like salts and detergents. An example of the results of washing the sample after it has been deposited on the matrix is shown in **Figure 4.5**. It is worth noting that water wash of a peptide mix can cause loss of hydrophilic peptides.

On-Plate Sample Wash

As can be seen from **Figure 4.5**, on-plate washes with cold water can be quite effective for removing salts from MALDI matrix solutions. What follows is a simple washing procedure.

- Deposit 0.5 μL of the analyte followed by 0.5 μL matrix* and allow to dry.

- Load the sample and analyze it. Check crystal appearance in magnified view.

- If results and/or crystals are of poor quality, pipette 2-3 μL of distilled water on top of the sample.

- Allow the droplet to stand for ~30 seconds to 1 minute.

- Pipette the water droplet in and out a few times to wash the matrix solution surface.

- Pipette the water off the sample, trying to remove as much as possible. Add a small amount of matrix, if necessary.

- Allow to dry and analyze. The wash steps can be repeated if necessary, but do not add matrix more than once.

* **Note**: we find that commercially available α-cyano matrix to typically be of low purity, a hot ethanol precipitation can enhance their performance. You will also notice that the α-cyano now is a bright yellow color instead of brown.

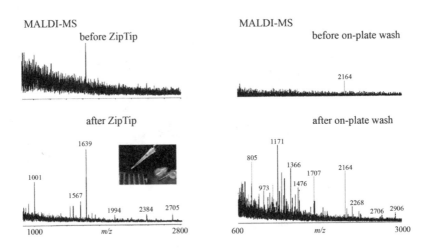

Figure 4.5. (left) MALDI-MS of a tryptic digest of 5 pmol of BSA before and after processing with C18 ZipTip. (right) MALDI-MS before and after an on-plate wash of an unknown results in the identification of mSin3A mouse protein using database searching.

ZipTip™ Sample Wash

Another popular approach for cleaning samples prior to analyzing them by MALDI or electrospray is using a ZipTip™. ZipTip™ pipette tips are 10 µL (P-10) pipette tips with a bed of resin fixed at the end of each one such that there is no dead volume. ZipTip™ Pipette Tips are useful for concentrating, desalting and fractionating picomole amounts of peptide, protein or oligonucleotide samples prior to analysis. In operation, ZipTips are affixed to a single or multi-channel pipette. Sample is aspirated and dispensed through the tip to bind, wash and elute the analyte(s) of interest. The concentrated, purified sample is precisely eluted in 1-4 µL of eluant. The working volume range of a ZipTip™ is between 1 to 100 µL and availability includes C_{18} and C_4 resins. The maximum molecular weight of a polypeptide which can be processed in ZipTip™ C_{18} is typically 50,000 Da and each tip can only be used to concentrate and desalt a sample once, which is performed in about a minute. For electrospray mass spectrometry the appropriate eluant for peptides is 50% ACN/0.1% TFA or 0.1% formic acid and for proteins 75% MeOH/0.1% TFA or 0.1% formic acid. Elution volumes for ZipTip™ Pipette Tips are typically 2-4 µL. A minimum sample amount for ZipTip™ C_{18} is approximately 30 femtomoles of ACTH or angiotensin. In general, 1 pmol of sample should provide an adequate signal. Recoveries of 75% are typical for concentrations above 5 pmol/µL. At concentrations of 0.25 to 2.5 pmol/µL, recoveries of 45-50% have been observed.

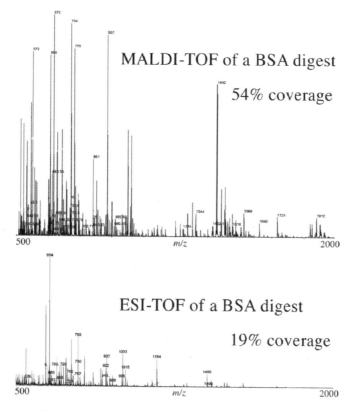

Figure 4.6. MALDI and direct infusion ESI-TOF mass spectra of a BSA tryptic digest illustrates MALDI utility for mixture analysis. ESI mass spectral data of the same digest gave significant signal suppression of the ions, while MALDI provided more comprehensive coverage. This effect can vary significantly depending on sample, solution and analysis conditions, however, in general MALDI provides better signals in simultaneous mixture analysis.

In addition to excellent sensitivity, MALDI has other useful features and capabilities for peptide and protein analysis. One of the most attractive features is its ability to analyze complex mixtures, typically with less signal suppression than ESI (**Figures 4.2 & 4.6**), making it extremely useful for biological samples such as protein digests. An illustration (**Figure 4.7**) of mixture analysis is shown with protein ladder sequencing, where a mixture of peptides/proteins differs in size by a single amino acid. This is primarily used for C-terminal sequencing with exopeptidase digestion.

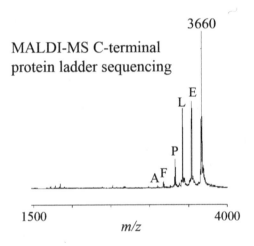

Figure 4.7. Positive ion MALDI-MS ladder sequencing data using the carboxypeptidase Y digestion of the peptide ACTH (7-38) provides some C-terminal sequence information.

Accuracy is also important in peptide and protein analysis. MALDI mass analysis (**Figures 4.2-4.5**) is typically performed with time-of-flight on proteins or TOF-reflectron analyzers on peptides with resolving capabilities on the order of 400 to 10,000 respectively and accuracy ranging from ±0.2% to 0.001% respectively. The resolution and accuracy depend upon the type of instrument being used (e.g. low resolution TOF versus a higher resolution TOF reflectron), the presence of an internal standard, buffers, salts, contaminants, the size/type of peptide/protein, and the selection of matrix material.

106

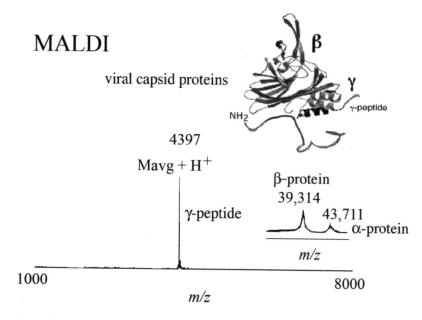

Figure 4.8. MALDI time-of-flight MS data showing viral capsid proteins using sinapinic acid matrix. The data demonstrates the simultaneously acquisition of proteins of significantly differing size.

Another important feature for protein/peptide analysis is mass range (**Figure 4.8**). MALDI-TOF can routinely analyze compounds from a mass of 700 to 200,000 Daltons or greater whereas MALDI-TOF reflectron is useful up to ~5000 m/z. The fact that MALDI predominantly generates ions that are singly charged makes it easy to identify individual peptides or proteins. MALDI is also the most reliable technique for analyzing glycoproteins, where the extreme broadness in their peaks reflects the carbohydrate heterogeneity in the proteins (**Figure 4.9**).

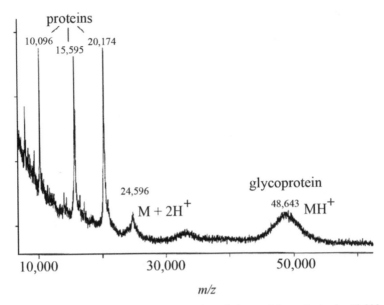

Figure 4.9. MALDI-TOF MS data showing a broad glycoprotein peak at m/z ~48,600 and proteins at m/z 10,096, 15,595 and 20,174 which contain no glycosylation. The broadness of the glycoprotein peak is due to carbohydrate heterogeneity on the protein.

Peptides and Proteins by Electrospray

MALDI and ESI are very different types of ionization sources for peptide and protein analysis, with each having specific advantages over the other. Perhaps the most important of these advantages include MALDI's ability to handle complex mixtures directly while ESI best handles mixtures when interfaced with liquid chromatography. In the low mass range, MALDI matrix interference effects measurements below m/z 700 making ESI more desirable. Another consideration is that ESI is a softer ionization method and is more suitable for the analysis of noncovalent complexes. For protein analysis, ESI analysis also tend to provide better resolution and accuracy since the measurements are performed on multiply charged species in a region (below m/z 3000) where the mass analyzer has high resolving power (**Figure 4.10**).

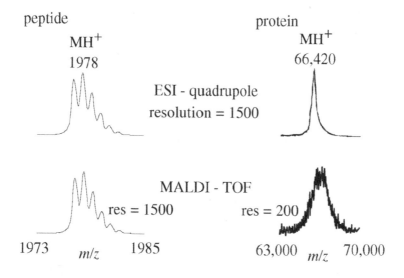

Figure 4.10. A direct comparison of peptide and protein data obtained from ESI-quadrupole and MALDI-TOF mass spectrometers. The data for the peptide is quite comparable, while the extra broadness of the peak associated with the protein MALDI-TOF spectrum reflects its lower resolution and lower accuracy in the higher mass range. The ESI protein data is generated from multiply charged ions below m/z 3000.

ESI is also useful for peptide and protein analysis for the following reasons:

- compatibility with tandem mass analyzers

- high sensitivity (subpicomole with nanoESI)

- allows for multiple charging and therefore the analysis of proteins with limited m/z range analyzers

- multiple charging allows for more complete fragmentation with collision induced dissociation.

As with MALDI, the electrospray ionization of peptides and proteins involves the addition of a proton or multiple protons. Sample preparation is achieved by dissolving the sample in a protic volatile solvent system that is relatively homogeneous and contains less than one millimolar concentration of salt, although higher concentrations have been used (such as the volatile buffer NH$_4$Ac at 100 mM). However, some salts (alkali and alkaline) and phosphate buffers are more detrimental to signal due to signal suppression. Because of the good mass accuracy/stability associated with quadrupole analyzers and because ESI can be easily interfaced with liquid chromatography, electrospray is often the method of choice for peptides. (Sample spectra shown in **Figures 4.11-4.13**). Moreover, although more sample is typically consumed (~1 picomole) than with MALDI (< 1 picomole), there are only a few preparation procedures and no matrices for electrospray, making it a quick method for obtaining molecular weight information.

Multiple Charging

Another important feature of electrospray is its ability to generate multiply-charged species. Multiple charging makes it possible to observe large proteins with mass analyzers that have a relatively small m/z range. In addition, observing multiple peaks for the same peptide allows one to make multiple molecular weight calculations from a single spectrum. Thus, one can average these values and obtain a more accurate molecular weight. The question often arises, especially concerning the analysis of peptides and proteins, "How is the charge state of the observed ion determined?" There are two ways: by the isotope pattern or by calculating via adjacent charge states (**Figure 1.9**).

In the spectrum in **Figure 4.11**, two peaks are seen, one at m/z 1978 and another at m/z 990. It is often possible to look at the isotopic distribution of the ions. One mass unit separation at m/z 1978 and 1/2 mass unit separation at m/z 990 correspond to the 1^+ and 2^+ charge states, respectively. The resolving power of the common quadrupole electrospray mass spectrometers only allow for distinguishing between singly and doubly-charged species.

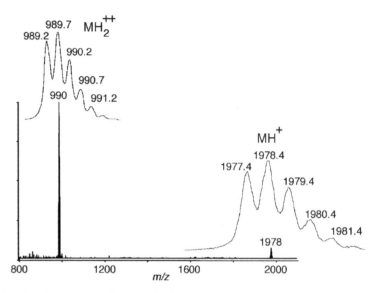

(molecular mass + #protons)/charge = mass-to-charge ratio

doubly charged	singly charged
(1976.4 + 2.0)/2 = 989.2	(1976.4 + 1.0)/1 = 1977.4
(1977.4 + 2.0)/2 = 989.7	(1977.4 + 1.0)/1 = 1978.4
(1978.4 + 2.0)/2 = 990.2	(1978.4 + 1.0)/1 = 1979.4
(1979.4 + 2.0)/2 = 990.7	(1979.4 + 1.0)/1 = 1980.4

Figure 4.11. The question of whether a peptide (or any other species) observed in the mass spectrum is singly, doubly, or multiply charged can be addressed in a several ways. In this spectrum it is possible to look at the isotopic distribution and determine the spacing between the isotopes. If isotopes are separated by one mass unit, the charge is 1+, if by 1/2 mass units, the charge is 2+. The calculations further demonstrate that the charge state can be determined from the isotope spacing.

Fortunately, as bigger peptides and proteins are analyzed, a distribution of multiply charged ions is obtained (**Figure 4.12**). Even though one cannot identify the individual charge states, from the isotopic pattern, unless using a high resolution FTMS instrument, the charge state can be deduced from distribution (**Figure 1.9**). **Figure 4.12** illustrates the results of two computer generated deconvolution calculations.

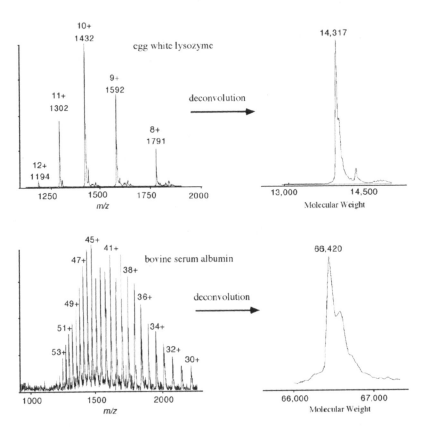

Figure 4.12. Electrospray mass spectra with the deconvoluted molecular weight spectrum of egg white lysozyme and bovine serum albumin (BSA).

Another advantage of generating multiply-charged ions with electrospray is that multiply charged peptide ions tend to give more complete fragmentation spectra. This has become increasingly important for *de novo* sequencing of peptides and protein identification.

One of the limitations of ESI in comparison to MALDI is its lower sensitivity. However, this has been overcome with the commercial introduction of nanoelectrospray ionization sources. NanoESI is a slight variation on ESI such that the spray needle has been made very small and positioned very close to the entrance of the mass spectrometer. The end result is increased efficiency which greatly reduces the amount of sample needed. The flow rates for nanoESI are on the order of tens of nanoliters per minute and the droplets are smaller than with normal ESI. Since the droplets are smaller with nanoESI, the amount of evaporation necessary to obtain ion formation is much less. As a consequence, nanoESI is more tolerant of salts and other impurities because less evaporation means the impurities are not concentrated as much as in ESI.

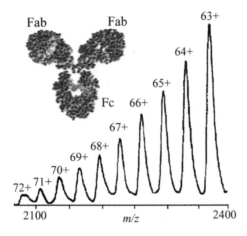

Figure 4.13. ESI mass spectrum of a IgG antibody with averaged molecular weight = 149,599 ± 12 Da. Adapted from Feng, R; Konishi, Y. "Analysis of Antibodies and Other Large Glycoproteins in the Mass Range of 150000-200000 Da by Electrospray Ionization Mass Spectrometry", *Analytical Chemistry*, 1992, 64:2090-2095.

ESI can also be applied to larger proteins. In fact, one of the largest proteins observed with ESI-MS has been with an IgG (**Figure 4.13**). However, direct analysis of these as well as glycoproteins by electrospray provides only limited information, and requires very high purity because excessively heterogeneous compounds produce complicated spectra due to multiple charging, often making interpretation difficult or impossible. In addition, sample heterogeneity will often reduce instrument sensitivity via signal suppression. In general, electrospray is not the method of choice and MALDI is typically used for the analysis of glycoproteins (**Figure 4.9**).

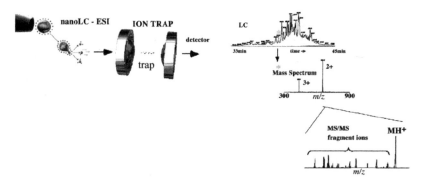

Figure 4.14. Interfacing liquid chromatography with electrospray ionization tandem mass spectrometry.

LC/MS

Another important feature of ESI-MS with regard to peptide and protein analysis is its ability to directly analyze compounds from aqueous or aqueous/organic solutions, a feature that has established the technique as a convenient mass detector for liquid chromatography (LC) (**Figure 4.14**). ESI or nanoESI combined with quadrupole or ion trap analyzers allows for MS analysis at flow rates ranging from 2 mL/min to 10 nL/min, respectively. The lower flow rates allow for high sensitivity measurements, such as in protein digest analysis, and the high flow rates allow for high throughput applications.

Declustering

As previously described, ESI induces ion formation from the generation of small charged droplets. Once ions are formed, they are subject to collisions as they enter the mass analyzer. These collisions can decluster aggregates, induce fragmentation, and change the charge states by removing protons. The kinetic energy of the ions can be adjusted to allow for some control over source fragmentation. This energy can be adjusted by varying the electrospray declustering or fragmentation potential. A diagram of the orifice is shown in **Figure 4.15**. However, it should be pointed out that this design is variable depending on the instrument, yet the same effect is observed in virtually all electrospray mass spectrometers. The energy of the ions entering the orifice is determined by the voltage applied to the orifice; the higher the energy, the more fragmentation is observed. In addition to inducing peptide fragmentation, increasing the declustering potential can cause the charge distribution of a protein to change. This is related to the greater collision-causing protons being stripped from the protein, and thus a shift in the charge state distribution occurs. **Figure 4.15** demonstrates that at a high declustering potential, protons are stripped from egg white lysozyme to produce a charge distribution completely different from one observed at a lower potential.

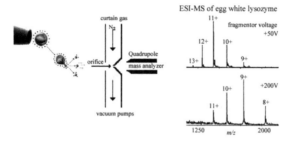

Figure 4.15. Orifice-induced collisions are controlled by the potential between the orifice and the quadrupole mass analyzer. The variation of this potential can affect sensitivity, the ability to observe noncovalent interactions, fragmenation, and charge state. The potential difference between the orifice and the quadrupole affects the energy of collisions prior to mass analysis. Electrospray mass spectra of egg white lysozyme at two different orifice (declustering) potentials demonstrates that at higher potentials, protons can be stripped from the protein thereby shifting the charge state distribution.

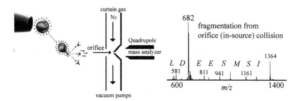

Figure 4.16. Collisions at the orifice can be useful for obtaining structural information. The collisions of this peptide, H-[ismseedllnak]-OH, have resulted in the formation of fragment ions from the N-terminal directly corresponding to its sequence. It is important to note that this is not a tandem mass spectrometry experiment and the fragment ions were generated as the ions entered the mass analyzer.

Another interesting aspect of the ESI source is that it can induce fragmentation of small peptides typically below a mass of 3000 Da. In relation to peptide/protein analysis, the declustering potential allows for peptides to be fragmented, thus allowing for sequencing information to be obtained. **Figure 4.16** illustrates how sequence information was obtained on a peptide simply by increasing this potential. A drawback of the application is that it can only be used on very pure samples; if the samples are not pure it may be easy to mistake an impurity for a fragment ion. When using orifice-induced fragmentation, identifying true fragment ions versus impurities is difficult. This problem can be overcome with the use of a tandem mass spectrometer. Sample purity is not as significant an issue with a tandem mass spectrometer since an ion of interest can be isolated even in the presence of several other ions (peptides). Once the ion of interest is isolated, it can be exposed to collisions and the resultant fragment ions can be mass analyzed. Tandem mass analysis and the specific applications of tandem mass spectrometry to peptides are described in the following section.

Overview

Mass spectrometry techniques such as ESI and MALDI have changed the way biochemists are approaching the challenges of protein/peptide analysis. The availability of these sensitive and gentle ionization methods have made it possible to analyze proteins and peptides through a range of available mass analyzers including TOFs, triple quadrupoles, quardupole ion traps, FTMS, and hybrid instruments. Furthermore, as shown in the next chapter, mass spectrometry is now routinely used in labs around the world as a fundamental tool for indentifying proteins. The high resolution and mass accuracy afforded by modern mass spectrometers have greatly facilitated its use for protein identification.

Questions

- What are some of the advantages of MALDI in peptide/protein analysis?

- What is the purpose of the MALDI on-plate sample wash?

- What challenge does glycoprotein analysis present?

- Why does ESI generally generate multiply-charged species of peptides and proteins?

- Why does ESI not generally generate multiply-charged species of small molecules?

- What affect does salts and buffers have on ESI signal?

- What is the challenge behind coupling MALDI with liquid chromatography.

- What is the advantage of ESI that allows it to be easily coupled with liquid chromatography.

Useful References

March RE & Todd JFJ (Editor). *Practical Aspects of Ion Trap Mass Spectrometry: Fundamentals of Ion Trap Mass Spectrometry. Volume I.* CRC Press: Boca Raton, **1995**.

Papayannopoulos IA. *The Interpretation of Collision-Induced Dissociation Tandem Mass Spectra.* Mass Spectrometry Reviews. **1995**, 14, 49-73.

Jensen ON, Podtelejnikov A, Mann M. *Delayed extraction improves specificity in database searches by matrix-assisted laser desorption/ionization peptide maps.* Rapid Comm. Mass Spectrom. **1996**, 10, 889-896.

Jonscher KR & Yates JR III. *The quadrupole ion trap mass spectrometer-A small solution to a big challenge.* Anal. Biochem. **1997**, 244, 1-15.

Cole RB (Editor). *Electrospray Ionization Mass Spectrometry: Fundamentals, Instrumentation, and Applications.* John Wiley and Sons: New York, **1997**.

Chapter 5

Protein Profiling

The absence of alternatives clears the
mind marvelously. - Henry Kissinger

Perspective

Mass spectrometry has rapidly become one of the most important tools for the identification of proteins (**Figure 5.1**) largely as a consequence of the completion of numerous genome sequences. Using ESI or MALDI-MS, intact proteolytic peptides can be vaporized and ionized into the gas phase and their masses accurately measured. Based on this information, proteins can readily be identified using a methodology called protein mass mapping or peptide mass mapping, in which these measured masses are compared to predicted values derived from protein databases. Further sequence information can also be obtained by fragmenting individual peptides in tandem MS experiments. In addition, large scale changes in protein expression levels (protein profiling) between two different samples can be assessed using quantitative tools such as two-dimensional gel electrophoresis (2D-GE) or stable isotope labeling in conjunction with mass spectrometric measurement.

Protein Characterization by Mass Spectrometry

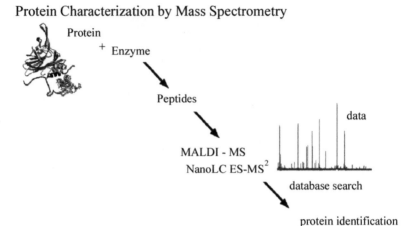

Figure 5.1. Mass spectrometry strategies used for protein identification.

Peptide Mass Mapping

Protein identification has traditionally been accomplished by subjecting proteolytic digests to high performance liquid chromatography (HPLC) followed by N-terminal (Edman) sequencing and/or amino acid analysis of the separated peptides. However, these techniques are relatively laborious, insensitive, and do not work with N-terminally modified peptides. More recently, mass spectrometry has been combined with protease digestion to enable peptide mass mapping. Definitively, peptide mass mapping (also known as protein/peptide mass fingerprint or PMF) combines enzymatic digestion, mass spectrometry, and computer-facilitated data analysis for protein identification. Sequence specific proteases or certain chemical cleaving agents (**Table 5.1**) are used to obtain a set of peptides from the target protein that are then mass analyzed. The enzyme trypsin is a commonly used protease that cleaves peptides on the C-terminal side of the relatively abundant amino acids arginine (Arg) and lysine (Lys). Thus, trypsin cleavage results in a large number of reasonably sized fragments from 500 to 3000 Daltons, offering a significant probability for unambiguously identifying the target protein. The observed masses of the proteolytic fragments are compared with theoretical digests of all the proteins listed in a sequence database (**Figure 5.2**). The matches or "hits" are then statistically evaluated and ranked according to the highest probability.

Table 5.1. Protease specificity. Proteolysis experiments can use any of a number of enzymes to perform digestion. The cleavage specificity of some of the different enzymes is denoted by a slash (/) before or after the amino acid responsible for specificity. Combinations of proteases can be used to reduce specificity and to mimic other proteases. For example, Lys-C and clostripain together are specific for the same sites as trypsin.

Protease	Amino Acid Specificity	Exceptions
Trypsin	X-**Lys**/-Y X-**Arg**/-Y	Does not cleave if Y = Pro
Endoproteinase Lys-C	X-**Lys**/-Y	Does not cleave if Y = Pro
Clostripain	X-**Arg**/-Y	
Endoproteinase Asp-N	X-**Asp**/-Y, X-**cysteic acid bonds**	Does not cleave if Y = Ser
CNBr	X-**Met**/-Y	Does not cleave if Y = Ser, Thr, or Cys
Glu-C (V8 Protease (E))	X-**Glu**/-Y X-**Asp**/-Y	Does not cleave if X = Pro
Pepsin	X-**Phe**/-Y X-**Leu**/-Y X-**Glu**/-Y	Does not cleave if Y = Val, Ala, Gly
Endoproteinase Arg C	X-**Arg**/-Y	Does not cleave if Y = Pro
Thermolysin	X-/**Phe**-Y X-/**Ile**-Y X-/**Leu**-Y X-/**Ala**-Y X-/**Val**-Y X-/**Met**-Y	Does not cleave if X = Pro
Chymotrypsin	X-**Phe**/-Y X-**Tyr**/-Y X-**Trp**/-Y X-**Leu**/-Y	Does not cleave if Y = Met, Ile, Ser, Thr, Val, His, Glu, Asp
Formic Acid	X-/**Asp**-Y	

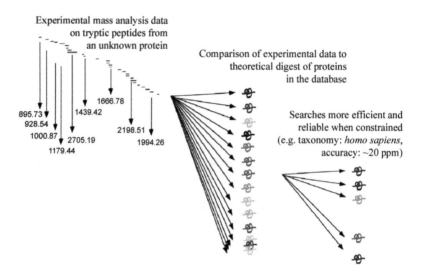

Experimental mass analysis data
on tryptic peptides from
an unknown protein

Comparison of experimental data to
theoretical digest of proteins
in the database

1666.78

895.73
928.54   1439.42
1000.87   2198.51
          2705.19
1179.44   1994.26

Searches more efficient and
reliable when constrained
(e.g. taxonomy: *homo sapiens*,
accuracy: ~20 ppm)

Figure 5.2. Protein identification through the comparison of tryptic peptides of an unknown protein to the theoretical digest of known proteins. The identification can be made to be more efficient and reliable when constraints are added such as the taxanomic category of the protein, as well as when high accuracy data and tandem mass measurements are used.

Clearly, the success of this strategy is predicated on the existence of the correct protein sequence within the database searched. However, the quality and content of such databases are continually improving as a result of genomic sequencing of entire organisms, and the likelihood for obtaining matches is now reasonably high. While exact matches are readily identified, proteins that exhibit significant homology to the sample are also often identified with lower statistical significance. This ability to identify proteins that share homology with poorly characterized sample species makes peptide mass mapping a valuable tool in the study of protein structure and function.

Upon submitting a query to a search program, a theoretical digest of all the proteins in the database is performed according to the conditions entered by the researcher. Variables that can be controlled include taxonomic category, digestion conditions, the allowable number of missed cleavages, protein isoelectric point (pI), mass ranges, possible post translational modifications (PTMs), and peptide mass measurement tolerance. A list of theoretical peptide masses is created for each protein in the database according to the defined constraints, and these values are then compared to the measured masses (**Figure 5.2**). Each measured peptide generates a set of candidate proteins that would produce a peptide with the same mass under the digestion conditions specified. The proteins in these sets are then ranked and scored based on how closely they match the entire set of experimental data.

This method of identification relies on the ability of mass spectrometry to measure the masses of the peptides with reasonable accuracy, with typical values ranging from roughly 5 to 50 ppm (5 ppm = ±0.005 Daltons for a 1,000 Dalton peptide). The experimentally measured masses are then compared to all the theoretically predicted peptide digests from a database containing possibly hundreds of thousands of proteins to identify the best possible matches. Various databases (**Table 5.2**) are available on the Web, and can be used in conjunction with such computer search programs as Profound (developed at Rockefeller University), Spectrum Mill (originated at University of California, San Francisco) and Mascot (Matrix Science, Limited). One obvious limitation of this methodology is that two peptides having different amino acid sequences can still have the same exact mass. In practice, matching 5-8 different tryptic peptides (within 50-100 ppm accuracy) is usually sufficient to unambiguously identify a protein with an average molecular weight of 50 kDa, while a greater number of matches may be required to identify a protein of higher molecular weight. It is important to note that the term protein identification as used here does not imply that the protein is completely characterized in terms of its entire sequence, as well as all its PTMs. Rather, this term typically refers to matching the peptides to some percentage of the amino acid sequence contained in the database. The entries in the database are both from direct protein sequence data (swissprot) and translated from genes (Genbank part of NCBI).

In theory, accurate mass measurements of the undigested protein could also be used for protein identification. In practice, however, the identification of a protein based solely on its intact masses is very challenging due to the stringent sample purity required, the need for extremely accurate mass measurements, and most importantly, the unpredictable variability introduced by numerous possible post-translational modifications. Also, even with the highest accuracy measurements, it becomes impossible statistically to measure the monoisotopic peaks for proteins greater than 15KDa. Average mass measurements are also not sufficient for protein ID.

Table 5.2. Two of the Protein Databases Available on the Internet.

NCBInr   A largely non-redundant database compiled by the National Center for Biotechnology Information (NCBI) by combining most of the public domain databases (Expressed Sequence Tags (EST's) not included).

Swiss Prot   A curated protein sequence database which strives to provide a high level of annotations, such as the description of the function of a protein, its domain's structure, post-translational modifications, variants, etc. This database offers a minimal level of redundancy and high level of integration with other databases.

Identification Using Tandem Mass Spectrometry

A more specific database searching method involves the use of partial sequence information derived from MS/MS data (**Figure 5.3**). As discussed later, tandem mass spectrometry experiments yield fragmentation patterns for individual peptides. Manual interpretation of a tandem MS experiment can often be quite difficult due to the number of different fragmentations that can occur, not all of which yield structurally useful information. However, analogous to peptide mapping experiments, the experimentally obtained fragmentation patterns can be compared to theoretically generated MS/MS fragmentation patterns for the various proteolytic peptides arising from each protein contained in the searched database. Statistical evaluation of the results and scoring algorithms using search engines such as Sequest (ThermoFinnigan Corp) and MASCOT (Matrix Science, Limited) facilitate the identification of the best match (**Figure 5.3**). The partial sequence information contained in tandem MS experiments is much more specific than simply using the mass of a peptide, since two peptides with identical amino acid contents but different sequences will exhibit different fragmentation patterns.

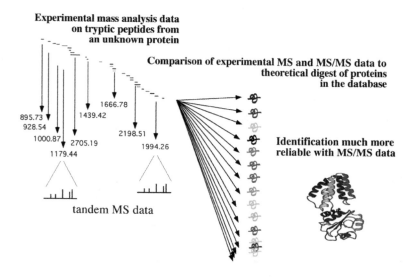

Figure 5.3. Protein identification through the comparison of tryptic peptides of an unknown protein to the theoretical digest and theoretical MS/MS data of known proteins, is even more reliable than just comparing the mass of the fragments.

While the molecular weight information obtained from ESI, and MALDI are useful in the preliminary stages of characterization, it can also be very important to gain more detailed structural information through fragmentation. Tandem mass spectrometry, the ability to induce fragmentation and perform successive mass spectrometry experiments on these ions, is generally used to obtain this structural information (abbreviated MS**n** - where **n** refers to the number of generations of fragment ions being analyzed).

One of the primary processes by which fragmentation is initiated is known as collision induced dissociation. CID is accomplished by selecting an ion and then subjecting that ion to collisions with neutral atoms. The selected ion will collide with a collision gas such as argon, resulting in fragment ions which are then mass analyzed. CID can be accomplished with a variety of instruments, most commonly using triple quadrupoles, quadrupole ion traps, Fourier transform mass spectrometry, and quadrupole time-of-flight mass analyzers. The quadrupole ion trap combined with electrospray ionization is currently the most common means of generating peptide fragmentation data, as they are capable of high sensitivity, and produce consistently high degrees of fragmentation information.

In order to obtain peptide sequence information by mass spectrometry, fragments of an ion must be produced that reflect structural features of the original compound. Fortunately, most peptides are linear molecules, which allow for relatively straightforward interpretation of the fragmentation data. The process is initiated by converting some of the kinetic energy from the peptide ion into vibrational energy. This is achieved by introducing the selected ion, usually an $(M + H)^+$ or $(M+nH)^{n+}$ ion, into a collision cell where it collides with neutral Ar, Xe, or He atoms, resulting in fragmentation. The fragments are then monitored via mass analysis. Tandem mass spectrometry allows for a heterogeneous solution of peptides to be analyzed and then by filtering the ion of interest into the collision cell, structural information can be derived on each peptide from a complex mixture. The fragment ions produced in this process can be separated into two classes. One class retains the charge on the N-terminus (**Figure 5.4**) and fragmentation occurs at three different positions, designated as types a_n, b_n, and c_n. The second class of fragment ions retains the charge on the C-terminus and fragmentation occurs at three different positions, types x_n, y_n, and z_n. The important thing to remember is that most fragment ions generated from ion traps, triple quadrupoles, QTOF's and FTMS instruments are obtained from cleavage between a carbonyl and a nitrogen (the amide bond). It is important to reiterate that when the charge is retained on the N-terminus this cleavage is a b-type, and when the charge is retained on the C-terminus of the peptide the cleavage is y-type.

Typical Peptide

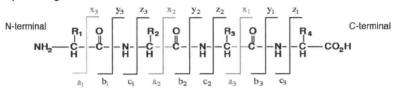

Peptide Fragmentation

Figure 5.4. Peptide fragmentation through collision-induced dissociation (CID) often results in the dominant fragmentation at the amide bonds in the polyamide backbone, producing ions of the type B or Y.

Certain limitations for obtaining complete sequence information exist using tandem mass spectrometry. In determining the amino acid sequence of a peptide, it is not possible for leucine and isoleucine to be distinguished because they have the same mass. The same difficulty will arise with lysine and glutamine (they differ by 0.036 Daltons) since they have the same nominal mass, although high resolution tandem analyzers (QTOF and FTMS) can distinguish between these amino acids. Another important point is that because a complete ion series (y- or b- type) is not usually observed, the combination of the two series can provide useful information for protein identification.

Separation

The Requirement for Sample Separation

Separation of proteins, or the peptides generated from a proteolytic digest, is especially important when trying to identify more than a couple of proteins simultaneously. Direct analysis by mass spectrometry in a typical biological sample is problematic due to the significant signal suppression caused by complex mixtures (**Table 5.3**). Tryptic digestion of a typical protein can result in the production of roughly fifty peptides, while miscleavages and various PTMs can give rise to many other unique species. Thus, biologically-derived samples can contain thousands to literally millions of individual peptides in the case of whole cell extracts. By comparison, even the tryptic digestion of approximately 3-5 proteins results in a peptide mixture complex enough to cause considerable signal suppression. Thus, samples of proteins (or peptides in a proteolytic digest) must be separated by gel electrophoresis or liquid chromatography prior to mass analysis.

Table 5.3. Protein Identification with MALDI and LC-MS/MS

	MALDI TOF reflectron	LC-MS/MS with an ion trap analyzer
Advantages	Very fast Widely available Easy to perform analysis High accuracy (10-50ppm) adds reliability to data Useful for a wide range of proteins Possible to reanalyze	In addition to molecular mass data, tandem MS measurements are performed in real time MS/MS information adds additional level of confirmation and good identification can be obtained on two to three peptides Multiple proteins can be analyzed simultaneously with simple reversed-phase LC run Useful for PTM identification High coverage of proteins (30% to 90%) depending on the protein and amount of protein
Disadvantages	Problematic for mixtures of proteins More peptides needed for reliable identification (5 to 8) Typically less coverage than LC- MS/MS approach	Computationally intensive; large database searches can take hours to days; relatively slow Analyses performed in real time from LC eluant so reanalysis not possible

Gel Electrophoresis

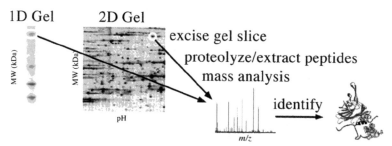

Figure 5.5. After performing SDS PAGE separation on a 1D (or 2D) gel, the stained portion of the gel representing the sample is cut out and then prepared for mass analysis by destaining, performing alkylation/reduction, in-gel digestion, and spotting on a MALDI plate. This can be done manually or robotically.

Gel electrophoresis is one of the most widely used techniques for separating intact proteins. In sodium dodecyl sulfate-polyacrylamide gel electrophoresis (SDS-PAGE), sometimes called one dimensional gel electrophoresis, the proteins are treated with the denaturing detergent SDS and loaded onto a gel. As a result, each protein becomes coated with a number of negatively charged SDS molecules directly proportional to its total number of amino acids. Upon application of an electric potential across the gel, all the proteins migrate through the gel towards the anode at a rate inversely proportional to their size. The separation is typically performed with multiple proteins of known masses run alongside the proteins of interest in order to provide a size reference. Upon completion of the separation, the proteins are visualized using any of a number of different staining agents (Coomassie, Sypro Ruby, or Silver), and the individual bands are physically excised from the gel. These excised spots are subjected to destaining, reductive alkylation, in-gel digestion, peptide extraction, and finally mass analysis for protein identification (**Figure 5.5**).

2-D Gels

The combination of SDS-PAGE electrophoresis with an isoelectric focusing step enables the separation of proteins of similar mass. In two-dimensional gel electrophoresis (2D-GE), proteins are first separated according to their isoelectric points (pI) by electrophoresis. In the electrophoresis step, each protein migrates to a position in the pH gradient corresponding to its isoelectric point. Once the isoelectric focusing step is complete, gel electrophoresis similar to SDS-PAGE is performed orthogonally to separate the proteins by size. Like 1D gels, 2D gel spots can be cut out, enzymatically digested, and mass analyzed for protein identification. Using this technique, thousands of proteins can simultaneously be separated and removed for identification.

In addition, 2D gels can help facilitate the analysis of certain PTMs. For example, differently phosphorylated forms of the same base protein may appear as a series of bands of roughly identical mass but different isoelectric points.

The primary application of 2D-GE is to assess large scale changes in protein expression levels between two different samples (i.e. healthy versus diseased samples). These protein profiling experiments (**Figure 5.6**) rely on the fact that the chemical stains (such as coomassie) used to visualize the separated protein bands produce responses roughly proportional to the total level of protein in the band. The experiments are typically performed by running 2D-GE on each of the samples and comparing the resulting patterns. Proteins bands that appear in only one gel or that differ significantly in their intensity are excised and identified. Alternatively, the two samples can be treated with different visualization agents (i.e. different dyes with significantly different fluorescent emission spectra), combined, and run on the same gel.

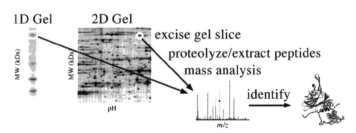

Figure 5.6. Protein profiling can be performed by comparing the 2D gel from two different cell lines. The protein spot of interest is excised from the gel and an in-gel proteolysis of the protein is performed.

Although still problematic, the reproducibility of 2D-GE has improved with the availability of high quality pre-cast gels, immobilized pH gradients strips (IPG), sophisticated pattern recognition software, and laboratory automation. However, considerable limitations remain, including operational difficulty in handling certain classes of proteins, the co-migration of multiple proteins to the same position, and potential unwanted chemical modifications. An even greater potential shortcoming of the classic 2D-GE technique is its inability to accommodate the extreme range of protein expression levels inherent in complex living organisms due to sample loading restrictions imposed by the gel-based separation technology employed. It is also worth mentioning that one doesn't always know the concentrations of the samples which can result in overloading the gel and streaking. Thus, 2D-GE separations often result in only the more abundant proteins being visualized and characterized. This limitation is of particular concern in that most interesting classes of regulatory proteins are often expressed at low concentrations.

Table 5.4. Protein profiling with gel electrophoresis and 2D LC MS/MS.

	2D Gels with Mass Spectrometry ID	2D LC MS/MS
Advantages	Widely available and becoming more reproducible. Software available for differential expression as well as quantifying differences (±20% at best). Easy visualization of up/down regulation demonstrated for highly complex mixtures.	Good dynamic range especially for low expression level proteins. (Codon Adaptation Index CAI of 0-0.2) very difficult for 2D gels to look below <CAI = 0.2. Good for a wide range of proteins with different hydrophobicities. MS/MS experiments performed automatically for reliable identification.
Disadvantages	Problematic for proteins with extremes of PI and MW. Difficult for hydrophobic proteins. Sample handling extensive for MS analysis (stain/destain and extraction), multiple steps required and time consuming. Also increases chance of keratin contamination. This can be minimized with use of robots. Overlapping proteins possible. Limited dynamic range.	Computationally intensive; database searches can take days; cluster computer systems not readily available. Multi-dimensional protein identification technology (MudPIT) has the potential of coupling to quantitative approaches. Currently limited application shown for differential protein expression (relative quantitation) with 2D LC/MS/MS for highly complex mixtures.

A Typical in-Gel Digestion Protocol for coomassie stained gels

1. Run gel and locate the protein bands of interest.
2. Excise bands of interest to 1 mm^2 pieces.
3. Destain by shaking for 10 minutes with 25 mM ammonium bicarbonate: 50% acetonitrile.
4. Discard – repeat until clear, rehydration of gel may be necessary.
5. Dessicate completely in speed vac.

6. Reduction: rehydrate in ~25 µl 10 mM dithiothreitol (DTT) or enough solution to cover the slices. Vortex, spin, and let reaction proceed 1 hr at 56 °C.
7. Alkylation: Remove DTT and add ~25 µL 55 mM iodoacetamide. Vortex, spin, and allow reaction to proceed 45 min. in the dark. Remove supernatant.
8. Wash gel slice with ~100 µL ammonium bicarbonate 10 min. Discard supernatant. Wash 2x with 25 mM ammonium bicarbonate/50% ACN. Speed Vac to dryness.
9. Rehydrate gel pieces in 25 mM ammonium bicarbonate pH 8.
10. Add 3 µL of modified sequence grade trypsin at 0.1 µg/µL.
11. Incubate at 37 °C overnight.
12. Transfer the supernatant to a new Eppendorf vial.
13. Extract the peptides using 50% acetonitrile/5% formic acid for 10 min. at 37 °C.
14. Combine with the supernatant liquid from step 11.
15. Dry to approximately 10 µL and then analyze.

Adapted from Anal. Biochem. 224, 451-455 (1995) and the web site of the UCSF MS Facility.

Protein ID

MALDI-MS

The ability to profile changes in the expression levels of thousands of proteins would be relatively meaningless without the ability to rapidly identify species of interest. To this end, automated liquid handling robots have been developed that perform all the sample preparation steps for peptide mapping experiments, including gel destaining, reduction/alkylation, in gel digestion, peptide extraction, and MALDI target plating. The benefits of such automation include less potential for contamination during sample preparation, increased reproducibility, rapid protocol development, and the ability to prepare hundreds of proteins in the course of one day. Whereas manual preparation would require a full week to perform two-hundred analyses, a robotics station can complete the task in less than one day.

Mass spectral data acquisition systems have similarly been automated to acquire spectra, process the raw data, and perform database searches for numerous samples. Commercial MALDI-TOF systems are currently available that can perform over 1,000 peptide mass mapping experiments in just twelve hours. These systems are able to perform automated calibrations, vary laser energies, and adjust laser firing location to maximize signal, with the entire data acquisition process requiring approximately 2 minutes or less. Similarly, automated data processing systems can recognize suitable signals, identify monoisotopic peaks, and submit summary peak lists directly to a search engine.

In the past, protein analyses were costly, time consuming and relatively insensitive. Today's high throughput proteomics systems enable researchers to investigate multiple unknown samples at once such as those coming from gels. Additionally, the flexibility of automated acquisition and data analysis software allows researchers to rapidly re-acquire and/or re-analyze entire batches of samples with minimal user effort.

LC MS/MS

An alternative approach to gel electrophoresis techniques involves the use of analytical separation methods such as liquid chromatography. Although the rest of this chapter focuses specifically on liquid chromatographic techniques, it is important to note that the same advantages also apply to other separation methods such as capillary electrophoresis. Although fast and often effective for the identification of individual proteins, direct MALDI analyses usually fail when dealing with more complex mixtures due to significant signal suppression. By contrast, LC-based methodologies fractionate the peptide mixtures before MS analysis, thus decreasing signal suppression and improving the analysis of any given peptide. More importantly, additional information is obtained on individual peptides by performing tandem MS experiments.

Whereas gel electrophoresis techniques separate intact proteins, liquid chromatography can be performed on the proteolytic peptides of these proteins. One of the most popular means of performing peptide LC-MS/MS involves the direct coupling of the LC to an ion trap mass spectrometer through an electrospray ionization interface. Other mass analyzers suitable for these experiments include triple quadrupoles and QTOF's. However, ion traps remain the most popular because of their ease of use, relatively low cost, and rapid scanning capability that enables tandem mass measurements to be performed in real time. For example, the ion trap first performs MS measurements on all the intact peptide ions. Then, in a second scan, it performs an MS/MS experiment on a particular peptide. This series of alternating scans can rapidly be repeated, with different ions selected for each tandem MS experiment. In this manner, single peptides from a complex mixtures can individually be addressed, fragmented, and analyzed.

The additional sequence information provided by tandem MS in the LC/MS experiments can be extremely powerful, sometimes enabling a definitive protein identification to be made on the basis of a single peptide. Obviously, tandem MS spectra of multiple peptides that arise from the digestion of a given protein provide greater opportunity for obtaining a definitive identification. Generally, fragmentation information can be obtained for peptides with molecular masses up to 2500 Daltons. Larger peptides can reveal at least partial sequence information that often suffices to solve a particular problem.

Although complete ion series (y-type or b-type) are usually not observed, the combination of the two series often provides useful information and sometimes the entire sequence. In addition, some amino acids as well as certain PTMs bias the fragmentation towards certain cleavages (loss of phosphate), dramatically decreasing the amount of sequence information obtained. Although chemical labeling techniques can partly compensate for these phenomena, it is important to note that not every peptide yields useful tandem MS spectra, thus further emphasizing the usefulness of attempting tandem MS on multiple peptides arising from a given protein.

2D LC-MS/MS

LC-MS/MS methodologies for protein identification have been extended to mixtures of even greater complexity by performing multi-dimensional chromatographic separations before MS analysis (**Figure 5.7**). As its name suggests, extremely complex tryptic digests are first separated into a number of fractions using one mode of chromatography, and each of these fractions is then further separated using a different chromatographic method. In theory, any combination of operationally compatible chromatographic methods possessing sufficiently orthogonal modes of separation can be utilized, and several different combinations have been described in the literature. However, the overwhelming number of studies to date have combined strong cation exchange (SCX) and reversed-phase (RP) chromatographies. More recently, further improvements have been realized by having both chromatographic beds in a single capillary column and directly coupling this column to an ion trap mass spectrometer. A step gradient of salt concentrations is used to elute different peptide fractions from the SCX resin onto the RP material, after which RP chromatography is performed without affecting the other peptides still bound to the SCX resin. The resulting nano-RP LC column effluent is directly electrosprayed into the mass spectrometer, making this method not only amenable to automation but also very sensitive. Using this "MudPIT" methodology (Multidimensional Protein Identification Technology), thousands of unique proteins have been identified from a whole cell lysate in a single 2D LC MS/MS experiment. Additionally, recent studies have also indicated that this technique possesses a greater dynamic range than that obtained using 2D gel electrophoresis, enabling the detection of lower abundance proteins. However, one limitation slowing this methodology's wide scale implementation is the computing power required to effectively compare tens of thousands of of tandem MS spectra experimentally generated. Fortunately, improvements in the data analysis algorithms are gradually solving this problem.

2-Dimensional ESI LC MS/MS

Figure 5.7. The proteolytic peptides separated by liquid chromatography and 2-D liquid chromatography are ionized using electrospray ionization and then subjected to tandem mass spectrometry (MS/MS) experiments. The data from the 1-D experiments can analyze up to 200 proteins simultaneously, while the 2-D experiments are capable of handling thousands of proteins.

Protein Profiling

Protein profiling studies can also be performed using multi-dimensional LC-MS/MS in conjunction with stable isotope labeling methodologies. Specifically, two samples to be compared are individually labeled with different forms of a stable isotopic pair, their tryptic digests combined before the final LC-MS analysis. This ideally results in every peptide existing as a pair of isotopically labeled species that are identical in all respects except for their masses. Thus, each isotopically labeled peptide effectively serves as its partner's internal standard, and the ratio of the relative heights of two isotopically labeled species provides quantitative data as to any differential change that occurred in the expression of the protein from which the peptide arose.

One approach towards differential labeling involves growing cells in isotopically enriched media. For example, one set of cells would be cultured in media that contained ^{14}N as the only source of nitrogen atoms, while the comparative case would be grown in media that only contained ^{15}N. Although effective in incorporating different stable isotopes into the two samples, the determination of which two peptides comprise an isotopically labeled pair is complicated by the fact that each pair exhibits a distinct mass difference depending on the number of isotopic atoms incorporated.

Alternatively, isotope-coded affinity tags (ICAT) (**Figure 5.8**) provides a more generally applicable approach based on the *in* *vitro* chemical labeling of protein samples. Specifically, ICAT utilizes the high specificity of the reaction between thiol groups and iodoacetyls (such as iodoacetamide) to chemically label cysteine residues in proteins with isotopically light or heavy versions of a molecule that differ only by the existence of eight hydrogen or deuterium atoms, respectively. The labeled protein samples are then combined and simultaneously digested, resulting in every cysteine-containing peptide existing as an isotopically labeled pair differing in mass by eight Daltons per cysteine residue. It should be noted that the general strategy of chemical labeling can be extended to other functional groups present in proteins for which chemical selective reactions exist, and several such approaches have been reported.

Due to the low natural abundance of cysteine compared to other amino acids, the overwhelming majority of the tryptic peptides remain unlabeled, and can interfere with the accurate determination of which two peptides comprise an isotopically labeled pair. Therefore, before the final LC-MS/MS analysis, an affinity selection is performed to selectively isolate the cysteine-containing species from the remainder of the tryptic peptides. In its original embodiment, a biotin molecule was also incorporated into the chemical label and used in conjunction with a monomeric avidin column to affinity purify the cysteine-containing peptides. Alternative approaches such as acid cleavable biotin are making ICAT easier to use. Although these solutions enable the accurate identification of isotopically labeled peptide pairs, they obviously preclude the analysis of proteins that do not contain cysteines and also greatly reduce the number of opportunities to effect LC-MS/MS identification of the proteins that do contain cysteine residues.

Protein Profiling with LC MS/MS and Isotope Labeling

isotope label two separate populations

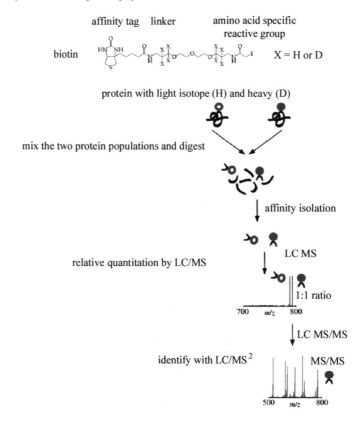

affinity tag   linker   amino acid specific
                             reactive group

biotin   X = H or D

protein with light isotope (H) and heavy (D)

mix the two protein populations and digest

affinity isolation

relative quantitation by LC/MS

LC MS

1:1 ratio

700   m/z   800

LC MS/MS

identify with LC/MS^2 MS/MS

500   m/z   800

Figure 5.8. The strategy for protein profiling using ICAT reagents was first proposed by Gygi *et al*. (*Nature Biotechnology*) and can be broken down into 5 parts. The reagents come in two forms, heavy (deuterium labeled) and light (hydrogen labeled). Two protein mixtures representing two different cell states treated with the isotopically light (open circles) and heavy (filled circles) ICAT reagents. An ICAT reagent is covalently attached to each cysteinyl residue in every protein. The protein mixtures are combined, proteolyzed and the ICAT-labeled peptides are isolated with the biotin tag. LC/MS reveals ICAT-labeled peptides because they differ by 8 Da. The relative ratios of the proteins from the two cell states are determined from the peptide intensity ratios. Tandem mass spectrometry data is used concurrently to obtain sequence information and identify the protein. A more recent version of ICAT containing C13 labeling allows for better co-elution of the unlabeled and labeled peptides.

LC-MALDI MS/MS

Several groups are exploring MALDI-based LC-MS/MS strategies that involve multidimensional separation by depositing the effluents of the final separation columns directly onto MALDI target plates (**Figure 5.9**). De-coupling the separation step from the mass spectrometer in this manner enables more thorough analyses of samples to be performed due to the removal of artificially imposed time restrictions. The resulting plates can also be reanalyzed as required without the need to repeat the separation step, thus decreasing sample requirements while focusing system resources only on the acquisition of tandem MS spectra of species of interest. An advantage of this approach is high throughput while the two main disadvantages are relatively poor MS/MS data from singly charged species typically generated from MALDI and quantitative analyses of protein content with MALDI is not as accurate as ESI based approaches.

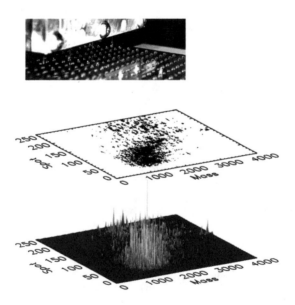

Figure 5.9. An example of HPLC MALDI-MS. (Top) Four µHPLC columns performing parallel deposition on 384 microtiter plate format for analysis by MALDI. (Middle & Bottom) Three-dimensional plot of the reversed-phase µHPLC–MALDI FT-ICR MS analysis of a tryptic digest of yeast proteins. Image courtesy of Eric Peters *et al.*.

Overview

Both MALDI and LC-MS/MS are playing important roles in protein identification and protein profiling. MALDI offers many advantages in terms of speed and ease of use, whereas, LC-MS/MS offers a more reliable protein ID as well as a greater potential for quantitative analysis and post-translational modification identification. LC-MS/MS currently appears to be the primary tool for profiling.

Questions

- What is peptide mass mapping?

- Why is trypsin commonly used as a protease in peptide mapping?

- How is tandem mass spectrometry useful in protein identification?

- Why is separation of the proteins/peptides important for mass spectrometry studies?

- What are some of the advantages/disadvantages of using 2D gels for protein profiling?

- What are some of the advantages/disadvantages of using LC-MS/MS for protein profiling?

- What are some of the potential advantages of a LC-MALDI approach for protein profiling?

Useful References

Gygi SP, et al. *Quantitative analysis of complex protein mixtures using isotope-coded affinity tags.* Nature Biotechnology. **1999**, 17, 994-999.

Yates 3rd JR. *Mass spectrometry: From genomics to proteomics.* Trends in Genetics. **2000**, 16, 5-8.

Voss T & Haberl P. *Observations on the reproducibility and matching efficiency of two-dimensional electrophoresis gels: consequences for comprehensive data analysis.* Electrophoresis. **2000**, 21, 3345-3350.

Gygi SP, Corthals GL, Zhang Y, Rochon Y, Aebersold R. *Evaluation of two-dimensional gel electrophoresis-based proteome analysis technology.* Proc. Natl. Acad. Sci. USA. **2000**, 97, 9390-9395.

Corthals GL, Wasinger VC, Hochstrasser DF, Sanchez JC. *The dynamic range of protein expression: a challenge for proteomic research.* Electrophoresis. **2000**, 21, 1104-1115.

Wall DB, et al. *Isoelectric focusing nonporous RP HPLC: a two-dimensional liquid-phase separation method for mapping of cellular proteins with identification using MALDI-TOF mass spectrometry.* Anal. Chem. **2000**, 72, 1099-1111.

Aebersold R & Goodlett DR. *Mass spectrometry in proteomics.* Chem Rev. **2001**, 101, 269-295.

Peters EC, Horn DM, Tully DC, Brock A. *A novel multifunctional labeling reagent for enhanced protein characterization with mass spectrometry.* Rapid. Commun. Mass Spectrom. **2001**, 15, 2387-2392.

Washburn MP, Ulaszek R, Deciu C, Schieltz DM, Yates 3rd JR. *Analysis of quantitative proteomic data generated via multidimensional protein identification technology.* Anal. Chem. **2002**, 74, 1650-7.

Peters EC, Brock A, Horn DM, Phung QT, Ericson C, Salomon AR, Ficarro SB, Brill LM. *An Automated LC –MALDI FT-ICR MS Platform for High-Throughput Proteomics.* LCGC Europe. **July 2002**, 2-7.

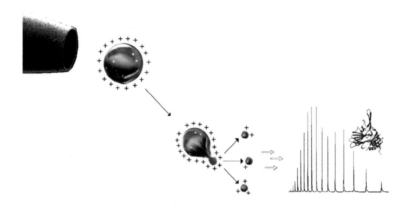

Chapter 6

Protein Structure Characterization

The only man who never makes a mistake is the man who never does anything. - *Theodore Roosevelt*

Perspective

Mass spectrometry is now commonly used for determining both the primary and higher order structures of proteins. The basis for these investigations lies in the ability of mass analysis techniques to detect changes in protein conformation under differing conditions. These experiments can be conducted on proteins alone such as monitoring charge state or in combination with proteolytic digestion or chemical modification. Proteases and chemical modification have long been used as probes of higher order structure, an approach that has been rejuvenated with the emergence of high sensitivity and accurate mass analysis techniques. Here, the applications of proteases and chemical modification with mass spectrometry are illustrated. For example, protein mass maps have been used to probe the structure of a protein/protein complex in solution (cell cycle regulatory proteins, p21 and Cdk2). This approach was also used to study the protein/protein complexes that comprise viral capsids, including those of the common cold virus where, in addition to structural information, protein mass mapping revealed mobile features of the viral proteins. Protein mass mapping clearly has broad utility in protein identification and profiling, yet its accuracy and sensitivity also allow for further exploration of protein structure and even structural dynamics.

Protein mass mapping combines enzymatic digestion, mass spectrometry, and sequence specific data analysis to produce and examine proteolytic fragments. This is done for the purpose of identifying proteins and, more recently, for obtaining information regarding protein structure. For protein identification, sequence-specific proteases are incubated with the protein of interest and mass analysis is performed on the resulting peptides. The peptides and their fragmentation patterns are then compared with the theoretical peptides predicted for all proteins within a database and matches are statistically evaluated. Similarly, the higher order structure of a protein can be evaluated when mass mapping techniques are combined with limited proteolytic digestion. Limited proteolysis refers to the exposure of a protein or complex to digestion conditions that last for a brief period; this is performed to gain information on the parts of the protein exposed to the surface.

The sequence specificity of the proteolytic enzyme plays a major role in the application of mass spectrometry to protein structure. A sequence-specific protease reduces the number of fragments that are produced and, concomitantly, not only improves the likelihood for statistically significant matches between observed and predicted fragment masses, but also reduces the opportunities for spurious matches. Another factor, the accessibility/flexibility of the site to the protease, also plays an important role in the analysis of structure. In this instance, ideally, only a subset of all possible cleavages are observed owing to the inaccessibility and/or inflexibility of some sites due to higher order protein structure. An example is illustrated in Figure 6.1, where asterisks mark potential cleavage sites that are exposed on the surface of a hypothetical protein. Since amino acids with hydrophilic side chains are found in greater abundance on the surface of proteins (at the solvent interface), proteases that cleave at hydrophilic sites are preferred in structural analysis. Trypsin and V8 protease, which cleave basic (K, R) and acidic sites (D, E), respectively, are good choices. Reaction conditions must be controlled to produce only limited proteolysis so that the cleavage pattern reliably reports on native tertiary structure. The cleavage of a single peptide bond can destabilize protein structure, causing local structural changes or even global unfolding.

Therefore, subsequent protease cleavage reactions would not inform on native structure.

theoretical proteolysis of a single protein

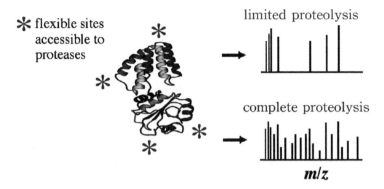

Figure 6.1. Illustration of the use of limited proteolytic cleavage as a probe of protein structure. The asterisks mark surface accessible loops that would be susceptible to proteolytic cleavage. Mass analysis of the limited proteolytic fragments yields a cleavage 'map' that provides information on structure. Complete digestion provides no structural information but is useful for protein identification.

Protein mass mapping can also be used to probe the quaternary structure of multicomponent assemblies such as protein-protein complexes, protein-DNA complexes and even intact viruses. The first application of limited proteolysis and MALDI mass spectrometry to the study of a multicomponent biomolecular assembly was performed by Chait and co-workers in 1995. In their studies, this combined approach was used to analyze the structure of the protein transcription factor, Max, free in solution as well as bound to an oligonucleotide containing its specific DNA binding site. The common feature when analyzing either protein-protein complexes or protein-DNA complexes is that the protease provides a contrast between the associated and unassociated states of the system. The formation of an interface between a protein and another macromolecule will protect otherwise accessible sites from protease cleavage and therefore provide information about residues that form the interface.

Recognizing Conformational Changes
with Mass Mapping

Protein mass mapping can be used to recognize simple conformational differences between different protein states. For example, X-ray crystallography data has shown that the protein calmodulin (CaM) undergoes conformational changes in the presence of calcium. The tertiary structure of calmodulin consists of an overall dumbbell shape (148 amino acids) with two globular domains separated by a single, long central alpha-helix connector (amino acids 65-92). It has been proposed that calcium-binding activates calmodulin by exposing hydrophobic residues near the two ends of the central helix. Mass maps resulting from digests by trypsin, chymotrypsin, and pepsin all demonstrated that the protein had undergone a tertiary structural change in the presence of calcium. **Figure 6.2** shows the trypsin digests of calmodulin in the presence and absence of calcium. Comparison of the two mass spectra reveals differences corresponding to cleavages in the central helical region of the protein. Based on the results of this relatively simple experiment, it can be appreciated that structural changes caused by Ca^{2+} binding within the dumbbell domains are propagated to the central helix, as manifested by altered protease reactivity within this latter structural feature.

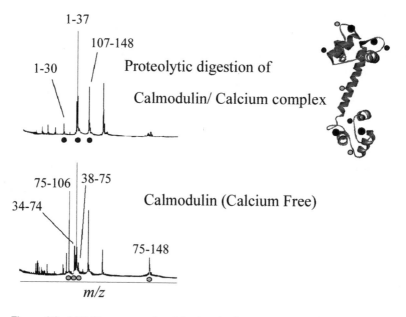

Figure 6.2. MALDI mass spectra of the trypsin digestion of calmodulin in the presence and absence of calcium. Differences are observed corresponding to cleavages within the central helical region of calmodulin (black dots) which are not observed in the presence of calcium (yellow dots) indicating a tertiary conformational change. Cleavage sites that are present in the Ca^{2+}/Calmodulin complex (black dots) and those that disappear upon addition of Ca^{2+} (yellow dots) are shown in both the spectra and the ribbon drawing. (Courtesy of J. Kathleen Lewis: Thesis, Arizona State University)

Electrospray ionization mass spectrometry has also been used to monitor protein folding and protein complexes. Early in the use of electrospray it was recognized that some proteins exhibit a distinct difference in their charge state distribution which was a reflection of their solution conformation(s). For example, two charge state distributions are shown in **Figure 6.3,** which depicts a protein's less charged native form and the more highly charged denatured conformation. The difference between the spectra is due to the additional protonation sites available in the denatured form. This phenomenon is demonstrated for the protein fibronectin where the charge distribution is maximized at the lower charge states at +6, and the denatured protein has a distribution maximized at a higher charge state of +10. There is growing recognition of the view that proteins function through a diverse range of structural states, from highly ordered globular structures to highly flexible, extended conformations. ESI-MS is a simple but highly sensitive and informative method to characterize the functional shape(s) of proteins (*i.e.* globular or extended) prior to more material-intensive and time-consuming spectroscopic or crystallographic studies.

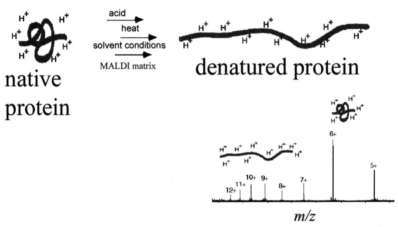

Figure 6.3. Electrospray mass analysis can be used to distinguish between native and denatured conformers of a protein. Denaturing a protein can often enhance ionization by dramatically increasing the number of sites available for protonation. The data shown represent both the native and denatured conformers of the fibronectin module. Adapted from Muir *et al.* (1995).

The use of hydrogen/deuterium (H/D) exchange to study conformational changes (**Figure 6.4**) in proteins or protein/protein interactions has been primarily performed using ESI-MS, although some studies have employed MALDI-MS. The concept of this approach is relatively simple in that amide protons within the portion of the proteins in close inter- or intra-molecular contact may form hydrogen bonds and will have different exchange rates relative to other more accessible regions of the complex. By monitoring this amide-hydrogen exchange, information can be gained on the noncovalent structure of a protein by itself or in a protein complex. It should be noted that while it is not possible through ESI-MS to monitor exchange in a residue specific manner, populations of protein molecules with distinct masses can be distinguished. The combined application of ESI-MS with NMR spectroscopy to monitor protein folding reactions using H/D exchange is particularly powerful. For example, Dobson, Robinson and co-workers characterized in detail transient protein folding intermediates for the protein egg white lysozyme using this dual approach. This was the first demonstration of discreet yet transient intermediates during a protein folding reaction. Importantly, these key findings were made possible only by complementing the more traditional NMR-H/D exchange approach with data from ESI-MS.

H-D exchange

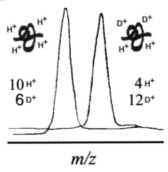

Figure 6.4. Theoretical mass spectra of two different populations of proteins – for native and denatured, where the native would be less susceptible to exchange.

Kriwacki *et al.* demonstrated the utility of limited proteolysis on the cell cycle regulatory proteins, Cdk2 and p21-B (**Figure 6.5**). Given the known protein sequence and the sequence specificity of trypsin, the mass measurement readily identifies the exact proteolytic site within each individual protein's sequence. The results revealed a segment of 24 amino acids in p21-B that is protected from trypsin cleavage, thus identifying the segment as the Cdk2 binding site on p21-B. The concepts illustrated in this simple example can be extended to much more complex systems, allowing insights into tertiary and quaternary structure to be obtained using picomole quantities of protein.

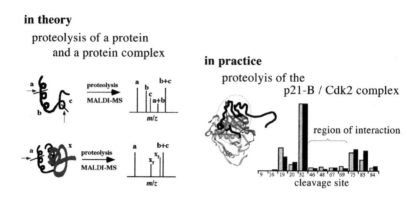

Figure 6.5. Probing protein/protein interactions using proteolysis and MALDI-MS. Schematic view (left) of key concepts. Two cleavage sites are accessible for the protein of interest alone (top), yielding five fragments after limited digestion. In the complex with protein X, one site is protected (bottom), yielding fewer fragments. However, fragments from protein X are also produced (X_f). Results represented as a histogram on the right indicate the "region of interaction" of p21-B with Cdk2 in a 24-amino acid segment (Kriwacki *et al.*).

Time-Resolved Mass Mapping of Viruses

Viruses also represent a noncovalent association of proteins for protein mass mapping structural studies. The proteolytic cleavage sites will reside on the exterior of the virus therefore giving insight into virus structure.

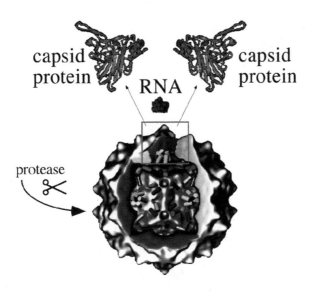

Figure 6.6. A nonenveloped icosahedral virus with a portion of the capsid proteins and RNA magnified above the virus. In protein mass mapping experiments, viruses undergo limited proteolysis followed by mass analysis of the proteolytic fragments. Time-resolved proteolysis allows for the study of protein capsid mobility.

Limited proteolysis/MALDI-MS experiments have been performed on human rhinovirus 14 (HRV14, aka common cold) and flock house virus (FHV). HRV14 and FHV both consist of a protein shell capsid, surrounding an RNA core (Figure 6.6).

Time-resolved proteolysis performed on HRV14 and FHV revealed many of the surface-accessible regions as anticipated; however, cleavages expected to be internal to the viral capsids (based on the crystal structures) were also generated. These data suggest that the internalized proteins are transiently exposed to the surface (**Figure 6.7**) when in solution. It is an observation impossible by x-ray crystallography and also it demonstrates the dynamic nature of the viral capsid.

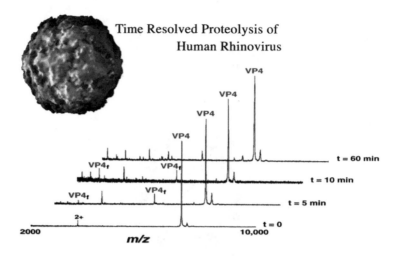

Figure 6.7. Trypsin digestion time-course of human rhinovirus. T = 0 represents MALDI mass spectrum of undigested virus with VP4 observed at m/z = 7390, VP1-VP3 (not shown) are observed at m/z = 32,518.9 (VP1 expected 32,519.5 Da), 28,475.9 (VP2 expected 28,477.4 Da), 26,219.5 (VP3 expected 26,217.8 Da). Interestingly, fragments from VP4 are the first observed in the limited digestion of the virus.

Chemical Cross-Linking and Modification

Other methods of probing higher-order structure include investigating the chemical reactivity of individual amino acids in protein and chemical cross-linking studies. Both approaches are possible since MS has proven to be a powerful method with which to characterize covalent post-translational modifications. Using such simple modification chemistries as acylation or succinylation, Glocker *et al.* have shown a clear correlation between the relative reactivity of specific amino acids and their accessibility to the protein surface (and solvent). A simple illustration of such reactivity is shown for a viral protein (**Figure 6.8**) after being exposed to acetylation. This resulted in limited chemical reactivity and the potential for characterizing the surface by determining the sites of modification.

Acetylation of an intact virus

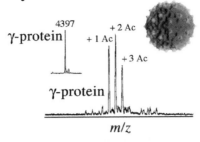

Figure 6.8. MALDI mass spectrum of a chemically modified viral protein from an intact virus. The sites of reactivity provide information about the surface-exposed topology of the virus.

Chemical cross-linking has been employed to determine the stoichiometry of oligomers with MALDI-MS analysis (**Figure 6.9**). MALDI-MS analysis of a complex before cross-linking allows for the determination of the molecular mass of the individual proteins. A cross-linking agent (such as glutaraldehyde) that reacts primarily with lysine to form cross-linking chains is added and then the reaction can be halted by the addition of the MALDI matrix.

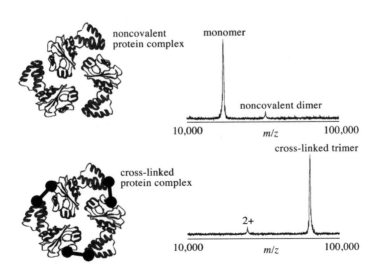

Figure 6.9. An example of how cross-linking of a noncovalent complex of proteins can alter the MALDI mass spectrum and provide the number of subunits in the complex.

Overview

The utility of combining proteolysis as well as chemical modification methods with MS analysis is becoming useful in structural studies of proteins. It is important to note that the key concepts of the methods are straightforward and the probing reactions are simple to perform. In the early stages of structural studies, the MS-based probing methods are particularly well-suited to provide rapid access to low-resolution maps that can then be used to guide subsequent high resolution crystallographic or NMR studies. This stage may also be an end point in some investigations where the simple identification of interacting residues is the desired information. Probing studies have also been shown to provide insight into structural dynamics.

Questions

- How can limited proteolysis be used with mass spectrometry to gain protein structural information?

- How can H/D exchange be used with mass spectrometry to gain protein structural information?

- How can chemical modification be used with mass spectrometry to gain protein structural information?

Useful References

Miranker A, Robinson CV, Radford SE, Aplin RT, Dobson CM. *Detection of transient protein folding populations by mass spectrometry*. Science. **1993**, 262, 896-900.

Glocker MO, Borchers C, Fiedler W, Suckau D, Przybylski M. *Molecular characterization of surface topology in protein tertiary structures by amino-acylation and mass spectrometric peptide mapping*. Bioconjug Chem. **1994**, 5, 583-90.

Cohen SL, Ferre-D'Amare AR, Burley SK, Chait BT. *Probing the solution structure of the DNA-binding protein Max by a combination of proteolysis and mass spectrometry*. Protein Science. **1995**, 4, 1088-1099.

Muir TW, Williams MJ, Kent SB. *Detection of synthetic protein isomers and conformers by electrospray mass spectrometry.* Anal Biochem. **Jan 1995**, 1:224, 100-9.

Finn BE, Evenas J, Drakenberg T, Waltho JP, Thulin E, Forsen S. *Calcium-induced structural changes and domain autonomy in calmodulin.* Nat. Struct. Biol. **Sep 1995**, 2:9, 777-83.

Kriwacki RW, Wu J, Siuzdak G, Wright PE. *Probing Protein/Protein Interactions with Mass Spectromety and Isotopic Labeling: Analysis of the p21/Cdk2 Complex.* J. Amer. Chem. Soc. **1996**, 118, 5320.

Fontana A, et. al. *Probing the Conformational State of Apomyoglobin by Limited Proteolysis.* J. Mol. Bio. **1997**, 266 (2), 223-230.

Lewis JK. *Protein Structural Characterization Using Bioreactive Mass Spectrometer Probes.* Arizona State University Ph.D. Thesis Dissertation. **1997**.

Jonsson AP. *Mass spectrometry for protein and peptide characterisation.* Cell Mol Life Sci. **2001**, 58, 868-884.

Ho Y, et. al. *Systematic identification of protein complexes in Saccharomyces cerevisiae by mass spectrometry.* Nature. **2002**, 415, 180-183

Wang L, Pan H, Smith DL. *Hydrogen exchange-mass spectrometry: optimization of digestion conditions.* Mol Cell Proteomics. **Feb 2002**, 1:2, 132-138.

With the right genes, a high carb energy source, and not a little testosterone... snowboarder Josh Cameron catches some air.

Chapter 7

Nucleic Acids, Carbohydrates, and Steroids

Perspective

Mass spectrometry is now widely used in many areas of biomolecular research including protein and pharmaceutical analysis yet it is also well suited for a myriad of other molecules including oligonucleotides, carbohydrates and steroids. This chapter presents an overview of the common techniques used for these molecules, including electrospray ionization, matrix-assisted laser desorption/ionization, and negative chemical ionization gas chromatography mass spectrometry. Among the capabilities that these techniques provide include molecular weight determination, fragmentation, sequencing, and noncovalent interactions.

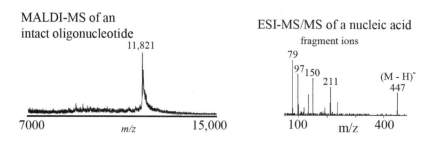

Figure 7.1. MALDI mass spectrum of an oligonucleotide and an ESI tandem mass spectrum of a modified nucleic acid. MALDI is particularly useful for oligonucleotide analysis because of its relative tolerance to impurities, salts and its sensitivity, while ESI is useful for nucleic acids because of their small size.

Oligonucleotide Analysis

Oligonucleotides are routinely assembled using automated solid phase DNA synthesis. In general, this technique is highly efficient, resulting in stepwise coupling yields of nucleotide phosphoamidite monomers as high as 99%. However, even with such efficient coupling reactions the theoretical yield for a 20mer is less than 90%. Errors in synthesis can also occur, resulting in a further decrease in the overall yield. Therefore, synthetic oligonucleotides require confirmation of purity and identity, which can be troublesome since the impurities frequently coelute on HPLC. The most common technique for oligonucleotide analysis is MALDI-MS, given that it is comparatively tolerant of mixtures, salts and impurities, although, ESI-MS and LC ESI-MS are also employed. In addition to structure confirmation, mass spectrometry is also being developed as a diagnostic tool for single nucleotide polymorphisms (SNP) analysis.

Oligonucleotide Analysis by MALDI-MS

As illustrated in **Figure 7.1**, MALDI-MS is typically the method of choice for intact oligonucleotide analysis. In addition to direct oligonucleotide analysis, it is possible with MALDI-MS to generate complete sequence information using an approach called "ladder sequencing," in which the results from different enzyme digestions of the oligonucleotide are combined. The use of multiple enzymes, specifically bovine spleen phosphodiesterase and snake venom phosphodiesterase, yields a stepwise sequence of peaks that directly correlate to the oligonucleotide sequence from either the 5' or 3' end. For instance, exposure to a high enzyme concentration results in significant digestion of the oligonucleotide. Subsequent digests of the oligonucleotides at lower enzyme concentrations generate enough information to sequence the entire oligonucleotide (**Figure 7.2**). The successively weaker enzyme solutions produce less digestion and therefore more information about the initial residues on the oligonucleotide termini. In MALDI-MS ladder sequencing experiments, no background signal was observed from either enzyme providing "clean" MS data, and the total amount of sample consumed was typically less than 2 nanomoles for the entire set of analyses (nine digests).

DNA analysis by MALDI-MS

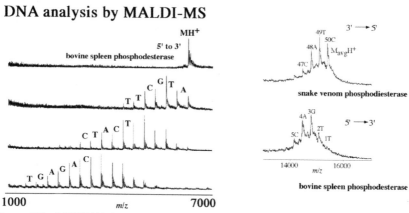

Figure 7.2. MALDI-MS (positive ion) of a ladder sequence where the order of the peaks corresponds to the sequence. The oligonucleotide ladder sequence 5' to 3' is generated from digestion using enzyme bovine spleen phosphodiesterase and the ladder sequence 3' to 5' is generated using the enzyme snake venom phosphodiesterase. The combination of the two can produce complete sequence information.

MALDI-MS ladder sequencing of a 50mer is shown in **Figure 7.2**, which illustrates that a ladder of approximately 5 residues from either the 5' or 3' end of the molecule was removed and observed. Typical of larger oligos, the signal intensities from the 50 and 40mer were less than those generated for the smaller oligonucleotides, which may account for the inability to detect more complete sections of the ladders. In addition, a significant amount of salt adducts were observed on the molecular ion, which resulted in significant peak broadening even after extensive desalting. An overview of the oligonucleotide MALDI-MS analysis and MALDI-MS ladder sequencing is provided in **Table 7.1**.

Another oligonucleotide application of MALDI-MS is the analysis of point mutations, known as single nucleotide polymorphisms (SNP's), which have been linked to diseases such as hypertension. Specifically, MALDI time-of-flight MS facilitates high-throughput mapping of SNP's. The time required for a typical MALDI-TOF-MS analysis is less than ten seconds and the detected masses are based on the absolute mass for the molecules being analyzed. The absolute mass can then be used to determine whether the point mutation exists (**Figure 7.3**). Additionally, all the steps required for complete analysis can be automated. MALDI-TOF-MS spectrum of an SNP analysis for hypertension is shown in **Figure 7.3**.

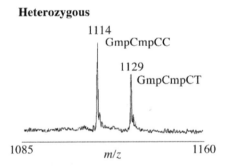

Figure 7.3. Example data obtained from the high throughput MALDI-TOF-MS analysis of single nucleotide polymorphisms (SNP's) used in disease diagnostics such as hypertension. This individual has both forms (heterozygous).

Oligonucleotide Analysis by ESI-MS

Electrospray mass spectrometry is also a useful tool in the characterization of oligonucleotides. Example applications of ESI-MS oligonucleotide analysis are shown in **Figures 7.1 & 7.4** with the analysis of a single nucleic acid and a megaDalton DNA molecule (uniquely performed by Henry Benner), respectively. In general, for molecular weight characterization, ESI-MS can be quite informative with respect to purity and confirmation. It is important to note that ESI-MS tends to be more sensitive to impurities than other ionization techniques and typically requires rigorous desalting to obtain quality mass spectral data. Another unique feature of ESI-MS spectra is the generation of numerous multiply-charged species (**Figures 7.5 & 7.6**). Conversely, MALDI-MS typically generates peaks that are dominated by the 1+ charge state (**Figures 7.1 & 7.2**).

Table 7.1. Characteristics of ESI and MALDI-MS oligonucleotide experiments. It should be noted that if nanoESI-MS^2 were used to perform the ESI studies, considerably less material (femtomoles) would have been consumed.

ESI-MS and ESI-MS/MS Oligonucleotide Analysis	MALDI-MS Oligonucleotide Analysis
Picomole to femtomole sensitivity	Picomole to femtomole sensitivity
Range to about 100 residues for intact molecule	Range to about 200 residues for intact molecule
Range to about 6 residues for MS/MS complete sequence information	Range to about 30 residues for complete sequence
Usually only partial sequence information obtained	Often full sequence information obtained. Interpretation of data is straightforward
Comments Interpretation of data is involved although computer deconvolution programs are available In an ESI study performed on representative oligonucleotides, no sequence on an 18mer - 50mer; Partial sequence on the 11mer; complete sequence on the 2mer - 6mers	Comments Partial sequence on the 50mer and 40mer; complete sequence on the 2mer - 30mer

ESI-MS of megaDalton DNA
using "Charge Detection"

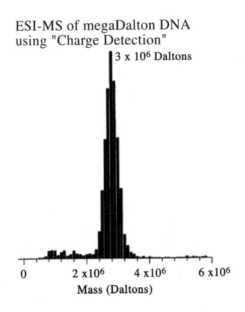

Figure 7.4. An ESI-MS spectrum from a 3 million Dalton DNA analysis. Henry Benner has created an instrument capable of analyzing megaDalton molecules (and even viruses) using ESI coupled to a special charge detection device that detects ions regardless of how big they are (Angew. Chem. 2001, 542). Routine ESI-MS oligonucleotide analyses are typically limited to a size of up to 30,000 Daltons and detection is very sensitive to concentration, impurities, and solvent conditions.

ESI-MS of a small oligonucleotide

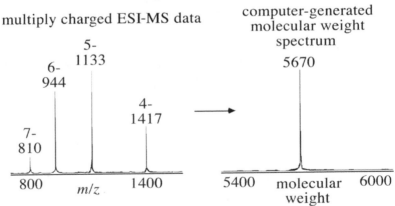

Figure 7.5. Electrospray ionization (negative ion) mass spectrum of an oligonucleotide. The computer-generated molecular weight spectrum was produced from the mass spectral data.

LC ESI-MS of oligonucleotides

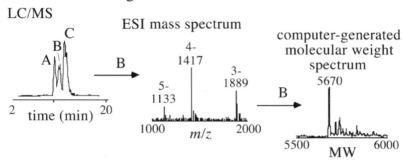

Figure 7.6. The LC ESI-MS of three oligonucleotides, the ion chromatogram, m/z data and the reconstructed molecular weight spectrum of the B oligonucleotide. Multiply charged ions representing negative charge states 3, 4, and 5 were observed.

Purification and characterization methods for oligonucleotides include liquid chromatography (LC), polyacrylimide gel electrophoresis (PAGE), capillary electrophoresis and dimethoxytrityl oligonucleotide purification cartridges. The effectiveness of these techniques is well known, yet they cannot unequivocally identify oligonucleotide composition or impurities. ESI-MS, and the more recent application of LC ESI-MS, can however provide enough information to verify base composition and purity. Direct ESI-MS analysis of unpurified oligonucleotides can give poor signals due to contaminating salts. Therefore, the use of LC can increase sensitivity as it serves to remove these salts and separate other contaminants prior to MS analysis.

Oligonucleotides and ESI-MS^2

ESI collision-induced dissociation (CID) tandem mass spectrometry has been used to determine sequence information from fragmentation patterns. ESI-MS^2 experiments have been performed on 50, 40, 30, and 20mer oligonucleotides (typically prepared in a 50:50 water:methanol solution). ESI-MS analysis gave excellent molecular ion signals corresponding to multiply-charged states (in negative ion mode) and accurate total molecular weight information. However, ESI-MS^2 provided virtually no sequence information on the 20, 30, 40, and 50mer

165

oligonucleotides. The results were not surprising given the size of the molecules and the low energy collisions generated in the triple quadrupole mass spectrometers.

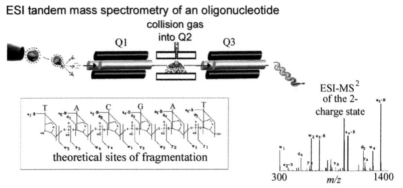

Figure 7.7. ESI-MS^2 (negative ion) data generated on the 6mer oligonucleotide 5'-TACGAT-3' using collision-induced dissociation on a triple quadrupole mass spectrometer. The theoretical fragmentation of this molecule is also shown.

ESI-MS^2 experiments have also been performed on smaller oligonucleotides including an 18, 11, 6, 4, 3, and 2mer. All of these oligonucleotides produced molecular ion signals in negative ion mode, while complete sequence information from ESI-MS^2 was possible only on the 6, 4, 3, and 2mer (the entire sequence and cleavage site information of the 6mer is shown in **Figure 7.7**. It should be noted that interpretation of the ESI-MS^2 results was typically more labor intensive (as compared to ladder sequencing) because fragmentation can occur at multiple sites on the phosphate, sugar, and base of the oligonucleotides. In contrast, MALDI ladder sequencing of the 20, 18, 11, and 6mer (**Figure 7.2**) was straightforward and complete sequence information was easily generated with excellent S/N and mass accuracy. It was possible to generate complete sequence information for the 4mer, 3mer and 2mer as well, however, the data were more challenging to interpret due to the background matrix interference in the low mass region.

Carbohydrate Analysis

Carbohydrates represent one of the largest and most important classes of biological molecules yet can be difficult to observe by mass spectrometry. The difficulty in their analysis largely comes from their polarity, a feature that can make them challenging to vaporize. In addition, even though they are highly polar, most carbohydrates are relatively neutral and therefore they have less of a proton affinity than peptides. Given these limitations, carbohydrates typically allow for a sensitivity that is at least two orders of magnitude lower than obtained by peptide mass analyses.

Depending on its structure, a carbohydrate can be ionized to give MH^+, M + alkali cation, M + ammonium ion, $[M-H]^-$, or M + chlorine anion. The choice of positive or negative ionization mode is highly dependent on the type of sugar. For example, neutral sugars generally give the positive ion $[M + Na]^+$ as the dominant ion with no significant formation of MH^+. Sugars containing carboxylic acids usually perform best in negative ionization mode to give $[M - H]^-$. ESI and MALDI-MS are capable of producing spectra from a wide variety of sugars and have detection limits down to the femtomole level. In addition, the mass accuracy can be 10 ppm or better depending on the mass analyzer. Fragmentation methods such as post-source decay, TOF-TOF, hybrid quadrupole time-of-flight (QTOF) and Fourier transform ion cyclotron mass spectrometry (FTMS) mass analyzers can provide useful structural information in the analysis of carbohydrates.

Carbohydrates by MALDI-MS and DIOS-MS

MALDI-MS analyses of carbohydrates commonly use 2,5-dihydroxy benzoic acid as a matrix. While both MALDI-MS and DIOS-MS are tolerant of contaminants such as salts and detergents, they can have significant detrimental effect on carbohydrate analysis. Although not necessary for the MALDI process, permethylation can be used to improve signal. However, complete permethylation is seldom achieved and therefore most researchers prefer to work with the underivatized sugars, MALDI-MS spectrum of a carbohydrate is shown in **Figure 7.8**.

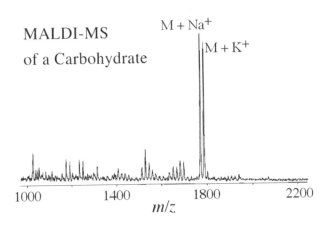

Figure 7.8. MALDI-MS of an underivatized carbohydrate.

MS of a Carbohydrate

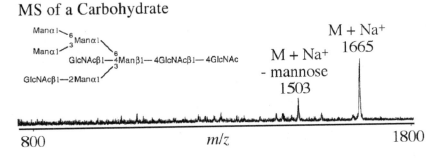

Figure 7.9. Monitoring a stereospecific enzymatic reaction of a glycosidase on an N-linked carbohydrate with DIOS-MS. The reaction involved exoglycosidase activity of mannosidase II and the reaction was performed directly on the surface with 30 pmoles of carbohydrate and approximately 1.5 pmoles of enzyme.

As shown in **Figure 7.9**, direct DIOS-MS analysis was used to monitor the exoglycosidase activity of 1-3-(1-6)mannosyl-oligosaccharide D-mannohydrolase (commonly known as mannosidase II) on an N-linked carbohydrate. The enzyme (molecular weight 190,000 Daltons) preferentially removes the 1→3 linked mannose residue from the non-reducing terminus.

Carbohydrate Analysis by ESI

While MALDI is quite popular and in some cases preferential for carbohydrate analysis, the most common method of analyzing carbohydrates is ESI. This may be due to the accessibility of ESI-MS instrumentation, the easier preparation of the sample with ESI and the greater availability of ESI instruments coupled with tandem mass analysis.

An Example of Monosaccharide Analysis with ESI

As is true for most carbohydrates, monosaccharides generally provide the best signal when complexed with an alkali cation. In a simple study of monosaccharide/alkali cation complex, the ability of galactose, mannose and fructose were shown to bind more effectively to the sodium cation than glucose. A variety of ESI-MS and ESI-MS^2 experiments were performed with D-glucose, D-galactose, D-mannose, and D-fructose and a deuterated analog of glucose, 6,6- D-glucose-d2 to aid quantitation. ESI-MS^2 experiments of the monosaccharides bound to the cation generated a distinctive fragmentation pattern which indicated dissociation of only the alkali cation with no significant cleavage of covalent bonds. The three monosaccharides— galactose, fructose, and mannose— generated monosaccharide/cation-to-cation intensity ratios such that $Na^+ > K^+ > Rb^+ > Cs^+$. This trend suggests that as the cation's atomic radius increases, the association with its host monosaccharide decreases. Interestingly, the results for D-glucose were similar, although, glucose had a lower affinity for Na^+. The discrepancy in Na^+ affinity between glucose and the three other monosaccharides indicates that their different isomeric conformations might influence the ability of the alkali ions to complex the monosaccharides, resulting in preferential cation binding (**Figure 7.10**).

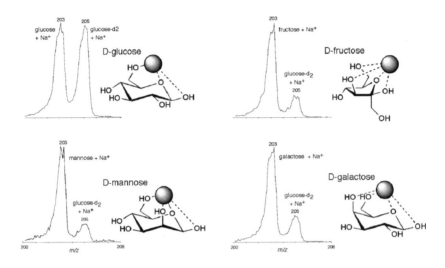

Figure 7.10. ESI tandem mass spectral data comparing the sodium cation affinity of glucose and its isomers, fructose, galactose and mannose. The electrospray tandem mass spectrum of [Na+ + D-6,6-glucose-d₂ + D-glucose], [Na+ + D-6,6-glucose-d₂ + D-fructose], [Na+ + D-6,6-glucose-d₂ + D-mannose], [Na+ + D-6,6-glucose-d₂ + D-galactose] generated fragmentation spectra demonstrating D-fructose, D-mannose, and D-galactose have a significantly greater affinity for Na+ than D-glucose. Structures were generated from these ESI-MS/MS data and molecular modeling studies.

Additional MS^2 experiments were performed on the monosaccharide heterodimer/cation complexes to further investigate preferential cation binding and to determine which monosaccharide had the greater cation affinity. The fragmentation analysis of the heterodimer/cation complex typically produced the [monosaccharide + Na]$^+$, [6,6-D-glucose-d$_2$ + Na]$^+$, and the precursor ion, [monosaccharide + 6,6-D-glucose-d$_2$ + Na]$^+$. The MS^2 analysis of the heterodimer complexes demonstrated significant preferential association to galactose, mannose and fructose as shown in **Figure 7.10**. Space filling models of the monosaccharide, as well as energy minimization calculations, further revealed that D-galactose, D-mannose, and D-fructose bound Na+ through a tetradentate complex, while D-glucose used a tridentate complex (**Figure 7.10**), which is consistent with the ESI-MS^2 data.

An Example of Complex Carbohydrate Analysis with ESI

Sialyl Lewis x (SLe^x) is a carbohydrate that exists on the surface of leukocytes (white blood cells) and is recognized as a ligand in the calcium mediated adhesion between leukocytes and endothelial (blood vessel) cells. SLe^x readily generates ions in both positive and negative ionization modes including [SLe^x + Ca - H]$^+$, [SLe^x + Na]$^+$, and [SLe^x - H]$^-$. Analysis of SLe^x has been performed using the MS^2 collision-induced dissociation (CID) capabilities of an ESI triple quadrupole mass spectrometer. Collisional activation of the Ca^{2+} complex, [SLe^x + Ca - H]$^+$, resulted in fragmentation with a characteristic loss of both fucose and sialic acid as the most abundant fragment ion (**Figure 7.11**). The collisional activation of the precursor anion, [SLe^x - H]$^-$, resulted in loss of Le^x, leaving only the sialic acid. MS^2 analysis of the monovalent cation complex, [SLe^x + Na]$^+$, resulted in fragmentation primarily through loss of sialic acid with some additional loss of fructose.

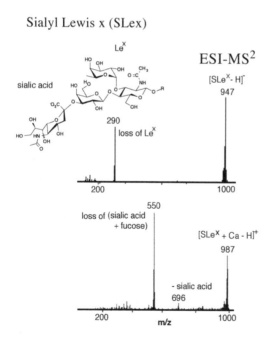

Sialyl Lewis x (SLex)

Figure 7.11. ESI MS^2 of Sialyl Lewis x (SLe^x) negative ion fragmentation of [SLe^x - H]$^-$ and positive ion fragmentation of [SLe^x + Ca - H]$^+$.

Analysis of Noncovalent Carbohydrate Interactions with ESI-MS

Le^x glycosphingolipids exist on cell surfaces and often exhibit extreme heterogeneity in their carbohydrate structures. The availability of synthetic, homogeneously pure glycosphingolipids and the capabilities of ESI-MS^2 allow for the investigation of calcium-mediated carbohydrate/carbohydrate interactions on the cell surface, which have been suggested to be precursors to cell-cell interactions.

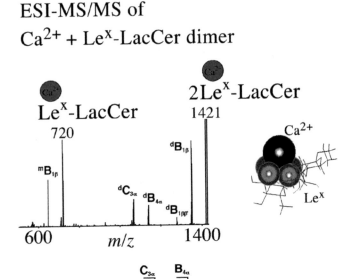

Figure 7.12. CID mass spectrum of the dimer [2Le^x-LacCer + Ca^{+2}]$^{+2}$ (m/z 1421) including fragmentation nomenclature; d designates that the fragment ion includes the noncovalent dimer, m designates that the fragment ion includes only the monomer and is no longer noncovalently bound to the other Le^x-LacCer. Inset is an energy minimized space-filling model of the calcium interactions with Le^x.

During the analysis of thsee molecules it was observed that the Le^x glycosphingolipid underwent significant homodimerization in the presence of calcium (**Figure 7.12**). In this process, a single Ca^{+2} cation binds the Le^x portion of the glycosphingolipid to promote association to form a homodimer. This associative behavior was specific for Ca^{+2} and, interestingly, was not observed in the presence of monovalent cations. MS^2 experiments on the $[2Le^x\text{-}LacCer + Ca^{+2}]^{+2}$ dimers resulted in the neutral loss of covalently and noncovalently bound species as shown in **Figure 7.12**.

Overall, carbohydrates can be challenging to analyze with mass spectrometry, yet, whether they are simple monosaccharides or more complex, ESI-MS, MALDI-MS and DIOS-MS have proven successful in their analyses.

Steroid Analysis

The detection and analysis of steroids have long posed a significant technical challenge due to their low concentrations, varied polarity, and presence in complex mixtures. The analysis of steroids and their metabolites in biological fluids has traditionally been carried out by gas chromatography GC/MS and more recently LC ESI-MS. Yet, each of these techniques requires derivitization of the steroid.

Steroids by GC Negative Chemical Ionization

Negative chemical ionization GC/NCI-MS is a standard mass spectrometric approach for analyzing steroids. NCI is performed in combination with perfluorophenyl derivatization (**Figures 7.13**) of the molecule to enhance its ionization properties. Although GC/NCI-MS is a very useful tool, the limitations to this approach include chemical preparation time and relative instability of the derivative.

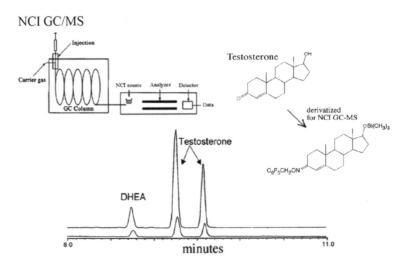

Figure 7.13. DHEA and testosterone (0.5 ng) were quantified using the *m/z* 535 ion. The deuterated internal standards, DHEA-d3 and testosterone-d3, were monitored at *m/z* 538. Adapted from Vallee *et al.* (2000) *Anal. Biochem.* 287:153.

GC NCI/MS can be a very efficient and sensitive approach toward detecting low level quantities of compounds (**Figure 7.13**). In NCI, a buffer gas (such as methane) reduces the energy of electrons in the electron beam, ultimately allowing for resonant electron capture by the analyte molecules. The buffer gas can also reduce fragmentation. Some of the benefits include high sensitivity, due to efficient ionization and less fragmentation than positive ion electron ionization or chemical ionization. Some of the limitations are that most volatile compounds do not efficiently produce negative ions and therefore require derivatization to facilitate electron capture.

Typical of these GC NCI/MS experiments is the requirement of chemical modification to improve sensitivity. The modification of the steroids to their pentafluorobenzyloxime/trimethyl silyl ether derivatives (**Figures 7.13** and **7.14**) facilitates electron capture and therefore enhances mass spectrometric analysis. Also, to further enhance sensitivity, the mass spectrometer can be operated in a selective ion-monitoring mode (SIM) which allows for picograms of steroids to be quantified from biological extracts.

Table 7.2. Approaches to Steroid Analysis.

	NCI GC/MS	LC ESI-MS
Sensitivity	femtomole to attomole	femtomole to attomole
Typical Chemical Modification	pentafluorobenzyloxime/tri methyl silyl ether	sulfation
Run Time	20-40 minutes	20-60 minutes
Tandem MS	fragmentation from ionization	MS^2 with ion trap or triple quadrupole
General Comments	low cost very good sensitivity, reliable, chemistry can be difficult	low cost very good sensitivity, well-suited for tandem mass spectrometry (MS^n)

Steroids by ESI

While NCI is popular for derivatized steroids (**Table 7.2**), ESI and nanoESI mass spectrometry are accurate and sensitive analytical techniques for steroid sulfates (**Figure 7.14**). Combined with precursor ion scanning, nanoESI provides low femtomole to attomole detection limits for charged compounds. By comparison, ESI and APCI are far less sensitive (picomoles), MALDI is relatively sensitive (low picomoles), although matrix interference in the mass range below 500 Daltons make MALDI an undesirable approach for this application.

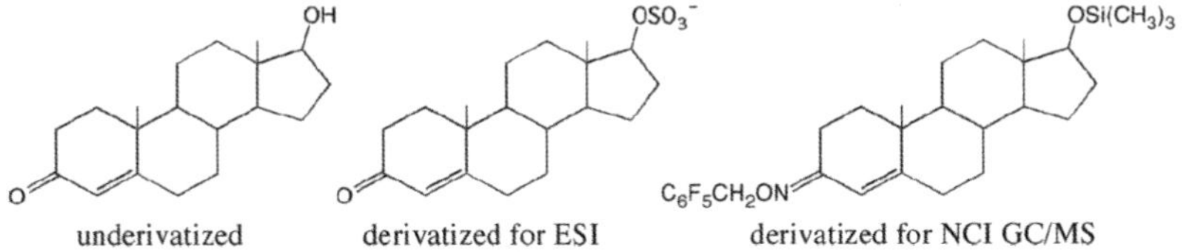

Figure 7.14. Testosterone as an unconjugated steroid, it's sulfated conjugate and perfluoro-phenyl derivative.

.

NanoESI for steroid analysis has been performed using precursor ion scanning on sulfated steroids where the sulfate fragment m/z 97 is used to generate spectra of its precursors, or "parent" ions. By employing precursor ion scanning, the interference from chemical noise is greatly reduced, thereby enhancing the signal-to-noise ratio. In negative nanoESI, the anionic species of steroid sulfates is observed and can be detected at concentrations lower than the protonated $[M+H]^+$ or $[M-H_2O+H]^+$ species of unconjugated steroids in positive mode. The formation of a sulfate functional group not only increases sensitivity, but also makes precursor ion scanning possible because the sulfate (HSO_4^-) fragment ion is observed in collision-induced dissociation tandem mass spectrometry (**Figures 7.15**). The combination of enhancements offered by sulfation and precursor ion scanning have allowed steroid analysis at the amol level.

Precursor ion scanning with a triple quadrupole

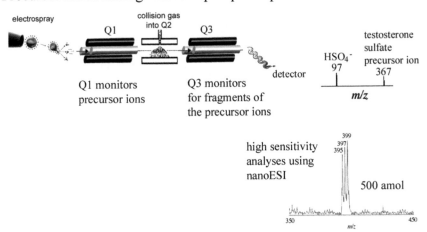

Figure 7.15. Precursor ion scanning illustrating that Q3 is held fixed on a particular fragment ion and Q1 is scanned to find the precursors to the fragment ion. In this case the sulfate anion [HSO4-] at m/z 97 is the fragment and testosterone sulfate (m/z 367) is the precursor. Negative ion nanoESI mass spectra (precursor ion scanning) of a mixture of pregnenolone sulfate (m/z 395), allopregnanalone sulfate (m/z 397), and d4-pregnenolone sulfate (m/z 399) at 500 amol/μl.

Overview

In previous chapters the focus was on the application of mass spectrometry to proteins and peptides, while this chapter further demonstrates the capabilities of mass spectrometry to oligonucleotides, carbohydrates and steroids analysis. ESI and MALDI are effective tools for oligonucleotides and carbohydrates yet steroids clearly are one of the more challenging biomolecules to analyze, largely because of their low ionization efficiency. Techniques such as ESI, MALDI, DIOS, and GC NCI/MS are all of value yet it is beoming apparent that for steroids derivatization is necessary for more efficient ionization.

Questions

- What mass spectrometry based approaches are used to sequence oligonucleotides?

- What is one of the disadvantages of ESI CID of oligonucleotides?

- What is an advantage of enzymatic digestion followed by MALDI analysis of oligonucleotides?

- Does carbohydrate heterogeneity in proteins presents a problem in structure determination?

- How is carbohydrate complexing to cations useful in mass analysis?

- What are some of the useful means of analyzing steroids and why is derivatization typically required?

Useful References

Pieles U, Zurcher W, Schar M, Moser HE. *Matrix-assisted laser desorption ionization time-of-flight mass spectrometry: a powerful tool for the mass and sequence analysis of natural and modified oligonucleotides.* Nucleic Acids Research. **1993**, 21, 3191-3196.

Siuzdak G, Ichikawa I, Munoz B, Caulfield TJ, Wong C-H, Nicolaou KC. *Evidence of Ca^{+2}-Dependent Carbohydrate Association through Ion Spray MS.* Journal of the American Chemical Society. **1993**, 115, 2877-2881.

Bothner B, Chatman K, Sarkisian M, Siuzdak G. *Liquid Chromatography Mass Spectrometry of Antisense Oligonucleotides.* Bioorganic and Medicinal Chemistry Letters. **1995**, 5:23, 2863-2868.

Owens DR, Wu JY, Phung Q, Siuzdak G. *Aspects of Oligonucleotide and Nucleic Acid Sequencing with MALDI and Electrospray Mass Spectrometry.* Bioorganic and Medicinical Chemistry. **1998**, 6, 1547-1554.

Schultz JC, Hack CA, Benner WH. *Mass Determination of Megadalton-DNA Electrospray Ions Using Charge Detection Mass Spectrometry.* J. Am. Soc. for Mass Spectrom. **1998**, 9, 305-313.

Chatman KS, Hollenbeck T, Hagey L, Vallee M, Purdy R, Weiss F, Siuzdak G. *Nanoelectrospray Mass Spectrometry and Precursor Ion Monitoring for Quantitative Steroid Analysis and Attomole Sensitivity.* Analytical Chemistry. **1999**, 71, 2358-2363.

Vallee M, Rivera JD, Koob GF, Purdy RH, Fitzgerald RL. *Quantification of neurosteroids in rat plasma and brain following swim stress and allopregnanolone administration using negative chemical ionization gas chromatography/mass spectrometry.* Anal. Biochem. **2000**, 287, 153-166.

Shen Z, Thomas JJ, Averbuj C, Broo KM, Engelhard M, Crowell JE, Finn MG, Siuzdak G. *Porous Silicon as a Versatile Platform for Laser Desorption/Ionization Mass Spectrometry.* Analytical Chemistry. **2001**, 33, 179-187.

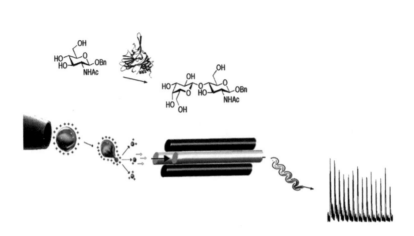

Chapter 8

High Throughput Analysis

Action, this day! - *Winston Churchhill*

Perspective

The development of high throughput mass spectrometry has been motivated largely by recent developments in both chemistry and biology. For instance, in chemistry, the production of large populations of molecular libraries increases the probability that novel compounds of practical value will be found, yet also requires that their identity be confirmed and purity assessed. While many fields of research have been influenced by this approach, the largest investment has come from the pharmaceutical, biotechnology and agrochemical arena. In the field of drug development, high throughput chemistry represents a convergence of chemistry with biology, made possible by fundamental advances in both automation and gene technology for cloning receptors. Mass spectrometry has played a key role in these advances. High throughput technology has even been extended to proteomics, where mass spectrometry is being used as a tool in rapid protein identification.

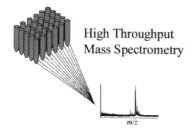

High Throughput
Mass Spectrometry

Figure 8.1. Mass spectrometry high throughput analysis involves the analyses of hundreds or thousands of compounds using atmospheric pressure ionization (API), liquid chromatography/mass spectrometry (LC/MS), or surface-based laser desorption/ionization (LDI) approaches such as MALDI or DIOS.

Electrospray ionization (ESI), atmospheric pressure chemical ionization (APCI), and matrix-assisted laser desorption/ionization (MALDI) mass spectrometry have become useful for qualitative, and more recently, quantitative analysis, aiding the development of mass spectrometry as a high throughput tool (**Figure 8.1**). Moreover, the advancement of these techniques has significantly extended MS applications toward a wide variety of challenging problems in drug discovery and also toward the identification of effective new catalysts and enzyme inhibitors. In addition, because MS-based methods do not involve chromophores or radiolabelling, they provide a viable and often simple alternative to existing analytical techniques which typically require extensive sample preparation and optimization time, the disposal of biohazardous waste, or a significant amount of sample.

In general, ESI-MS offers many advantages, including the ability to analyze low and high mass compounds, excellent quantitation and reproducibility, high sensitivity, simple sample preparation, amenability to automation, soft ionization, and the absence of matrix (as is necessary for MALDI). APCI, much like ESI, generates ions from a liquid stream, but is a somewhat harsh ionization technique than ESI. Because APCI imparts more energy into molecules for ionization than ESI, it is able to generate ions from less polar molecules than typically seen with ESI, but generally increases background signal. Fragmentation may occasionally occur using APCI, but the molecular ion is often still the most dominant peak observed. APCI is limited in its applicable mass range (<1000 Daltons) due to its inherently harsher ionization mechanism. A combined ESI/APCI source has been recently designed and commercialized promising the benefits of both ESI and APCI. A third atmospheric source, atmospheric pressure photoionization (APPI) has also begun to appear as a useful ionization tool. This source uses photons emitted from a krypton discharge lamp (10.0 and 10.6 eV) to ionize molecules, and has been shown to be effective for molecules difficult or impossible to detect using other atmospheric pressure ionization techniques.

MALDI and DIOS are especially well suited for the simultaneous analysis of multicomponent mixtures and commercial instruments are now available that offer automation capabilities. Since DIOS does not require a matrix, it does not create low mass interference and can therefore be used for small molecule analysis. Because MALDI and DIOS are scanning methods, they have the potential of offering ultra high throughput.

Automating Atmospheric Pressure Ionization

Sample Preparation/Instrument Configuration

"One bad apple does ruin the whole bunch" — Mike Greig (Pfizer)

The basic elements in successful mass analysis include sample solubility, sample purity, instrument calibration and sensitivity (which is relative to the amount of sample present). In automated mass spectrometry, where hundreds or thousands of analyses are performed each day, these elements become even more important. Sample solubility is a significant consideration, because if a single sample forms a suspension during analysis, the resulting particulates can damage the MS system by clogging sample transfer lines and autoinjectors. While filtering samples prior to their introduction into the MS system minimizes this problem, sample compatibility with system solvents is an important consideration.

Issues such as instrument calibration and sensitivity are primarily a matter of instrument maintenance and can be routinely monitored by incorporating standards at planned intervals.

Additional sample considerations in regards to automated analysis are: sample carryover, salt contamination, sample tracking, and robust rapid sample introduction into the analytical system. Carryover is just as detrimental to mass analyses as system clogging. Samples that easily ionize and are in solution at high concentrations are susceptible to carryover signal for subsequent analyses. The solution is simple – reduce sample concentrations. However, adhering to minimized concentrations can sometimes be difficult because the individual researcher may not always know exactly how much material is present. One approach to overcome this problem is to randomly monitor the UV absorption at the beginning of a large run, as high absorbance measurements of the initial samples can be used as criteria to shut down the system, send out a warning, or in more advanced systems, divert the flow to waste before the material reaches the mass spectrometer. Concerning salt contamination, some instruments can be surprisingly tolerant of high salt levels in solutions. Fortunately, the problem of salt inhibiting electrospray ionization can be easily avoided by several methods, including "Zip-tipping" (a form of micro solid-phase extraction) or performing LC/MS. In regards to sample tracking, it is best to institute a sample labeling system prior to beginning the analysis of a large number of samples. While this may seem obvious, organizing and putting a little thought into the labeling scheme can be very valuable.

One very simple sample tracking scheme is to use rack indexing, whereby large numbers of samples are submitted in standardized racks. Upon sample submission, each rack is given a rack number (usually based on chronological submission) and individual samples are numbered based on position in the rack. This system is particularly compatible with racks which conform to microtiter plate formats.

Another relevant question that is frequently asked in MS laboratories is whether to perform flow injection analysis or LC/MS. While LC/MS has become more rapid, often taking less than 5 minutes per run, flow injection is faster, typically requiring less than a minute per analysis (and in some cases 20 seconds). Also, with flow injection all the information pertaining to a sample can be obtained in one spectrum. The primary disadvantage is that significant signal suppression can occur when a complex mixture is introduced, thus resulting in a loss of information due to a lose of sensitivity. This is where LC/MS becomes especially advantageous with its ability to separate a mixture of components, but at a reduction in the speed of analysis and the addition of the time required to analyze the data.

The type of sample being analyzed is yet another consideration with automated API analysis. Typically the analysis of large molecules requires parameter manipulation, such as that of the fragmentor voltage (also known as orifice potential) to obtain a reasonably good signal. Small molecule analyses will often give good ion signals (typical ions observed are shown in **Table 8.1**) under a large variety of conditions and therefore are easier to automate.

Table 8.1. Ions typically monitored for automated mass analysis, with screening performed in both positive and negative ionization modes.

POSITIVE	NEGATIVE
[M + H]+	[M - H]-
[M + Na]+	[M + Cl]-
[M + K]+	[M + TFA]-

Further practical considerations for automated sample analysis include regulating flow rates, minimizing waste generation, venting, pump oil maintenance, solvent quality, safety, and comfort of the user. Lower flow rates require less solvent, which in turn generates less waste and minimizes some venting concerns. Of course, performing thousands of analyses at high flow rates requires consistent system maintenance, including ionization source cleaning and regularly scheduled pump oil changes, as pump oil breakdown can lead to many problems. Using high quality GC grade solvents (as opposed to LC grade which are only UV pure) is also advantageous for minimizing background ions which may be detected by MS. Importantly, safety and comfort around the instrument should be established as early as possible. Lastly, be sure to provide adequate space and ventilation around the instrument in order to access the system for inevitable problems that arise with all mass spectrometers.

General Data Analysis/Software/Storage

The ability to analyze the data from the mass spectrometer should be a major consideration when developing an automated mass spectrometry analysis system. While analytical instrumentation is becoming more reliable, MS system software is also constantly evolving. Therefore, it is becoming more important to define the problem and/or specific needs before searching for a system that will answer them. Whether it is to be used for routine batch analysis, high throughput pharmokinetic studies, or to search for new inhibitors, the software programs associated with each of the manufacturers' different mass spectrometers will allow these problems to be tackled in different ways, some faster and better than others.

Data storage can also become an issue when generating large or numerous data files. An average MS data file requires anywhere from 25Kb to 10Mb of memory storage, so even the large hard drives in modern PCs can be overwhelmed rapidly. Currently, the more expensive magnetic based storage tape drives are fast, easy to use and rewritable. However the low cost CD-based storage mediums are also attractive, so a decision can be made depending on the cost (CD) to "ease-of-use" ratio (magnetic) as to what is most important. The writing, transferring, and eventual deletion of massive amounts of data quickly leads to hard drives that can be fragmented causing PCs to slowly become sluggish and crash. Consequently, it is important to defragment hard drives on a regular basis using any of a number of commercially available software packages.

Typical Equipment for Automated API analyses

API-MS systems may be configured with various mass spectrometers, each of which has its benefits and limitations. The quadrupole is by far the most commonly used mass analyzer because of its low cost, manageable size and robustness for coupling to liquid chromatographs. A quadrupole can provide adequate mass resolution, mass accuracy, and excellent quantitation, but it is not the MS of choice for applications that require high accuracy measurements (**Table 8.2**). More importantly, the primary limitation of the quadrupole is its low sensitivity when detecting across a broad mass range, which may be a serious consideration when the mass of interest is not known in advance. As an alternative, both the quadrupole ion trap and the time-of-flight (TOF) mass spectrometers are viable analyzer options which address some of the inherent limitations of the quadrupole. Ion traps provide the unique means to perform multiple stages of tandem MS for fragment identification. However, the ion trap still requires slow scanning for higher mass resolution and thus may not be ideally suited for high speed analysis. In the movement towards high-throughput analysis, TOF systems have become increasing popular because they tackle many of the limitations of the previous two MS instruments. As a pulsed detector, TOF scan speeds are exceedingly fast, on the order of milliseconds. This pulsed detection does not discriminate against ion mass and so the m/z

range is infinite, a feature unique to TOF analyzers. Lastly, with improved electronics incorporated into today's TOF systems, mass accuracy has been significantly enhanced and TOF MS is used routinely for mass accuracy measurements (10 ppm).

Table 8.2. General comparison of API mass analyzers. It should be noted that performance can vary significantly for different commercial systems.

	Accuracy	Resolution	*m/z* Range	Tandem MS	Scan Speed
Quadrupole	0.01%	4000	4000	MS^2	seconds
Comments -	Large dynamic signal range, small size, relatively low cost. Has proven to be robust in combinatorial library analysis.				
Ion trap	0.01%	4000	4000	MS^4	seconds
Comments -	Limited dynamic signal range, small size, relatively low cost, well suited for tandem mass spectrometry. Somewhat useful for combinatorial library analysis.				
TOF-reflectron	0.001% or better	15,000	10,000	MS^2	milliseconds
Comments -	Very fast scan speed, simple design, good resolving power.				

1 Million Analyses/Year: A Case Study

The task at hand was to analyze one million discrete compounds derived from high throughput chemistry in one year using an MS-based technique. If one were to assume the syntheses yielded pure, or at least very clean reactions, the obvious choices would be to use either a rapid flow injection technique with any number of different types of instruments, or DIOS coupled with rapid sample preparation. In reality, where reaction yields can be anywhere from 10-90%, a chromatography based MS technique will produce the best results when estimating purity. The three choices reviewed here are multiple LC/MS systems using a durable single quadrupole mass spectrometer, multiple LC systems flowing into a single MUX (or multiplexing system), multiplexed MS, or ultra-high speed super critical fluid chromatography (SFC) with a time-of-flight MS.

The simplest and most dependable method of achieving this throughput goal would be to use eight separate LC/MS systems. This option provides the most flexibility, as any combination of LC mass spectrometer brands and types can be put into service with any combination of API sources. Additionally, should one system break down, there would be seven remaining systems continuing to produce data. Since modern LC/MS systems are quite robust, inexperienced operators can still obtain quality data. Assuming a 3 min cycle time (time from injection to injection) on a system running an average of five days a week for 24 hours each day, eight systems could analyze 992,000 samples in one year. Although a seemingly simple solution, it would take considerable man power (to load instruments, analyze data, and perform preventative maintenance) to keep these systems operational. Additionally, data would be produced on eight different instruments, and the required laboratory space and capital investment for these systems is quite large.

A second option would be to use a single 8x MUX MS system fed by eight HPLCs. For ESI-only systems, a MUX, is currently one of the more advanced for rapidly sampling from numerous HPLCs with one mass spectrometer (**Figure 8.2**). The concept is simple in that multiple ESI sources are placed around the entrance to a TOF mass analyzer. Then each source is sampled by moving a rotor that allows only one ESI source to spray into the mass analyzer at a time. The advantages of this setup are that as many as eight different LC systems can be analyzed in parallel, one data set is acquired using a single data station, it needs relatively little bench space, and one skilled operator can keep the system operational. The disadvantages are that while this wheel is spinning, each channel is sampled less than 1/8 of the time, resulting in fewer data points across each peak. Because of this, slower LC methods must be employed, resulting in a "fast" run with a cycle time of five minutes. Using the slower LC method, this system could analyze about 750,000 compounds/year running in the same time frame as previously described. The second and major disadvantage is if the system or any single component is inoperative, there is no back-up system and no data will be produced until the entire system is repaired.

Liquid Chromatography ESI MUX mass spectrometry

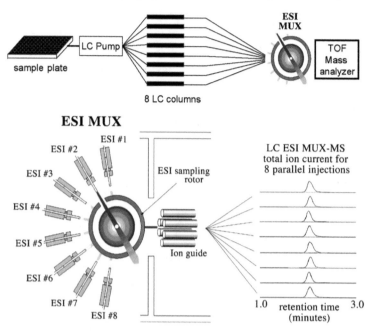

Figure 8.2. Multiplexing ESI sources onto a single mass spectrometer is one way of increasing sample throughput. This example shows eight ESI heads going into one time-of-flight mass analyzer. The mass analyzer samples each ESI head via a rotor that rapidly moves from one ESI port to another.

A third, lesser known option, is to couple supercritical fluid chromatography with an API-TOF MS. SFC is rapidly gaining popularity in the pharmaceutical industry due to its high speed and applicability to most drug like chemicals. SFC is applied to relatively hydrophobic molecules (such as drugs) and SFC is a normal phase chromatographic technique that uses compressed CO_2 as the non-polar mobile phase which is then modified by a polar solvent such as methanol. Because of the higher diffusivity and lower viscosities achieved by the mobile phase, SFC can be run at much higher flow rates than standard LC, with higher resolution. Running at 10 ml/min with a methanol gradient from 5-60% over thirty seconds, a forty second cycle time was achieved while still providing good resolution (**Figure 8.3**). At this rate, with two instruments, 1.2 million samples per year could be analyzed. This system has several advantages over the previous two described above. Since there are duplicate systems, a single system breakdown will not completely compromise data acquisition. Only one or two skilled operators are needed, and the capital outlay is much lower than the previous options. Another major advantage comes in solvent usage and waste production. Both the MUX and multiple LC/MS systems require eight HPLC systems, each consuming a considerable amount of organic solvent. Two SFC systems, while at a much higher flow rate, consume about 17% of the organic solvent. This solvent consumption can be reduced even further without sacrificing speed by operating SFC in a microbore mode. ESI, APCI, and APPI have all been demonstrated to work well with SFC, so unlike a MUX system, there is a choice of API source. A current disadvantage of an SFC/MS system is that there are very few commercially supported systems available and few operators experienced with both SFC and MS.

Supercritical Fluid Chromatography Mass Spectrometry

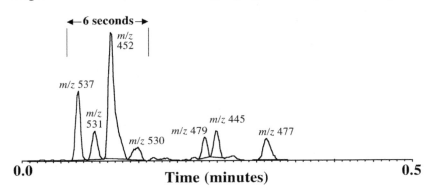

Figure 8.3. Analysis of a complex mixture by the ultra-fast SFC method. SFC uses compressed CO_2 as the mobile phase which is then modified by a polar solvent such as methanol to generate a gradient. Measurement of baseline separation of four eluting compounds within a window of 6 seconds is also facilitated by the fast 0.05 sec/scan data point sampling using an APCI-TOF-MS.

ESI-MS as an Assay for Enzyme Inhibitors

One specific application of automated ESI-MS is the investigation of enzyme inhibitor libraries. In this approach, the enzymatic mixture (substrate, inhibitor, product, and internal standard) is introduced into the ESI mass spectrometer while analyzing product formation as a function of the presence of inhibitor. Since product formation is quantitatively monitored, the effectiveness of the inhibitor can be readily determined.

As an example, this has been applied to monitor inhibitors of galactosyltransferase and fucosidase enzymes (**Figure 8.4**). Both enzymes are responsible for processing cell-surface carbohydrates, which in turn are associated with many specific recognition and signaling processes leading to biological functions and disease. Current assays for the quantitation of glycosyltransferase activity require separation of the compounds, use of radiolabeled sugars, performance of large scale reactions, or the use of additional enzymes.

The galactosyltransferase catalyzed reaction was examined in the presence of potential inhibitors. The 20 inhibitor candidates and 2 control reactions of the initial inhibitor library were assayed individually in 22 parallel reactions (**Figure 8.4**), and then quenched by adding MeOH (followed by the addition of an internal standard). The reaction mixtures were then injected directly into the electrospray mass spectrometer with an autosampler. The concentrations of the inhibitors were varied in order to determine the IC_{50} (inhibitor concentration at 50% inhibition).

Either one inhibitor or multiple inhibitors can be screened simultaneously. For example, reactions that contained 5 inactive compounds showed no inhibition, whereas reactions containing 4 inactive compounds and 1 active inhibitor showed inhibition. The compounds in the inhibited reaction were then individually analyzed to identify the actual inhibitor compound. Such strategies significantly increase the screening capacity up to 3600 inhibitors/day. The effectiveness of this method can be extended. The only criterion of this approach is that the molecule of interest is ionizable.

191

Monitoring Enzyme Inhibition

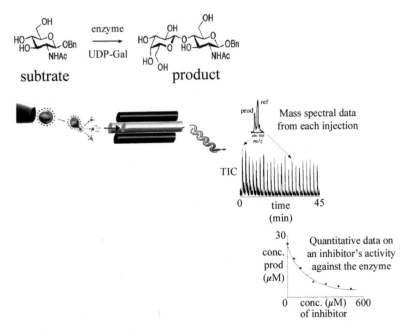

Figure 8.4. Monitoring enzyme reaction as a function of inhibitor present. ESI-MS total ion current generate mass spectra for each reaction containing a different inhibitor. Quantitative data on the product of the galactosyltransferase catalyzed enzyme reaction produced kinetic data on the effective of the inhibitor.

Automating Surface Based Desorption/Ionization

The most useful attributes of MALDI and DIOS are their ability to analyze complex heterogenous mixtures and to scan the surface containing sample quickly. Scanning the surface allows for analysis rates exceeding one sample per second.

In the examples discussed, API-MS was the mass spectrometric method of choice mainly because of its ability to analyze low mass compounds and its amenability to coupling with a chromatographic system. As the following section will show, MALDI-MS, although requiring the use of matrix, or DIOS, which requires no matrix, offer many of the same advantages (automation, soft ionization, and excellent quantitation) and in addition are able to analyze high mass compounds and relatively heterogenous mixtures.

Pattern Searching

The automation of MALDI and DIOS analyses is becoming increasingly important in both proteomics and combinatorial chemistry. Typically, the instrument is designed to search for a signal from each sample well. Analyses are driven by a computer-controlled procedure that monitors for the ion signal as a function of laser position and laser intensity. To accomplish this, the computer workstation automatically adjusts laser intensity and searches the sample well until a signal (within the specified mass range and intensity threshold) is obtained **(Figure 8.5).** Based on careful preselection of autosampler options from manual analysis of the sample, each parameter (laser intensity, search pattern and step size in well, and signal within a specified *m/z* range) is adjusted to minimize time of analysis and maximize signal quality.

Figure 8.5.
Three different parameters automatically adjusted and monitored on a laser desorption/ionization system:

1) laser position
2) laser intensity
3) *m/z* & ion intensity range

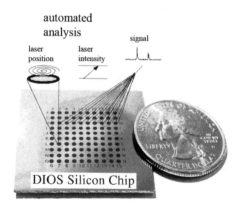

In an example of MALDI and DIOS automation procedures, the laser intensity was initially at a minimum energy setting of ~ 2 µJ/pulse and was then increased up to a maximum of 50 µJ/pulse (as controlled by a variable neutral density filter) in step sizes of five increments, resulting in an increase in laser intensity of approximately 10 µJ/pulse per step. The laser intensity was increased until an acceptable data signal was acquired, whereby if no signal was observed, the laser beam was repositioned on the well and the analysis resumed at the lower laser power. To adjust the laser position on the sample plate, a pre-programmed spiral search pattern was used which began in the center of each circular well and spiraled outward in 0.2 mm increments. For each sample well analysis, only signals that reached a specified intensity were saved and once this signal was observed the analyses would automatically move to the next well. If the intensity is not achieved within approximately 10 seconds the analyses would automatically move to the next well.

Automated Quantitation Studies using MALDI-MS

Since some biofluids contain interfering substances, it is often necessary to perform extractions prior to sample analysis. In such instances, the development of an efficient extraction step can be very time-consuming. In an effort to create a simpler and more efficient protocol, a combinatorial extraction method was used with automated MALDI mass spectrometry to improve quantitative clinical analysis of the immunosuppressant drug cyclosporin A (CsA) from blood. This combinatorial-extraction approach was followed by analyses using a MALDI mass spectrometer equipped with automated multi-sampling capabilities to facilitate data collection and analysis of cyclosporin A (**Figure 8.6**). The organic layer extracted from each blood sample was placed on a MALDI sample plate. Extraction optimization was performed by generating an array of solvent systems, followed by automated analysis to identify the most successful extractions.

The first generation of experiments revealed four binary solvent systems to be effective for cyclosporin extraction (hexane/EtOH, ACN/H$_2$O, ACN/MeOH, hexane/CHCl$_3$). A new array based on these solvent systems was generated and in a second iteration of experiments, hexane/CHCl$_3$ (70:30) was found to provide the most effective and rapid single-step extraction for cyclosporin and its metabolites. The limits of detection were determined to be 15 ng/ml in whole blood for both ESI/MS and MALDI-MS.

Optimizing Cyclosporin A Extraction from Blood

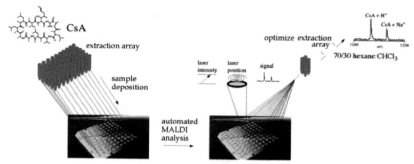

Figure 8.6. Automated MALDI mass spectrometry experiments, performed as a function of laser position (within each well) and laser intensity for each extracted CsA sample. The first iteration of these extraction experiments generated four useful solvent systems, and the second generation of these experiments produced an effective 70:30 hexane/CHCl$_3$ extraction solvent system.

Automated genotyping using MALDI-MS

As discussed in Chapter 7, single nucleotide polymorphisms (SNPs) are point mutations in the genetic material of individuals. These mutations appear with variable frequency between 1 in every 300-1000 nucleotides within the human genome, making them the most common type of human genetic variation. While many genetic variances have little functional relevance, some have been linked to particular diseases, such as Cystic Fibrosis, Muscular Dystrophy, Alzheimer's Disease, and many forms of cancer including breast, ovarian and prostate cancer. Because SNPs are defined mutations both in type and locality of the changes, they will provide a rapid method for mapping genetic variability in a population and for determining genetic susceptibility to disease. For this reason, a massive effort has been underway to determine high throughput methods for mapping SNP mutations throughout the genome.

To enable genome wide genetic studies using SNPs, dense genetic maps are needed, consisting of at least 1 informative SNP per 30 kilobases (1 x 10^5 total SNPs). In addition, to determine the clinical relevance of SNPs, comparative studies of the genetic differences between thousands of affected and unaffected individuals are needed.

These undertakings require robust, flexible and inexpensive assays and platforms providing a high degree of multiplexing. The time required for a typical MALDI-TOF analysis is less than ten seconds, and the masses detected are based on the absolute mass for the molecules being analyzed. Most importantly, all the steps required for complete analysis can be automated. An example of MALDI-TOF analysis of an SNP on the human β-2 adrenergic receptor is shown in **Figure 8.7**. SNPs in the human β-2 adrenergic receptor are linked to a genetic predisposition to hypertension and are also implicated in cardiovascular disease.

Common SNP analysis methods currently include the PinPoint assay and the simplified GOOD assay. The PinPoint assay, based on the addition of a single nucleotide to a genotyping primer, is complementary to the PCR analysis of point mutations, the products of which are short oligonucleotides. The simplified GOOD assay is a purification-free, three-step method (PCR, primer extension and phosphodiesterase II digestion) performed in a single tube, and immediately followed by MALDI analysis. For MALDI analysis of SNPs, the reaction mixture can be diluted in acetonitrile and then transferred onto MALDI target plates prepared with matrix, such as α-cyano-4-hydroxy cinnamic acid methyl ester. Alternative matrix mixtures are 3-hydroxypicolinic acid in a 1:1:2 mixture of water, acetonitrile and 0.1M ammonium citrate, and 10 mg/ml sinapinic acid in 2:1 water/acetonitrile solution.

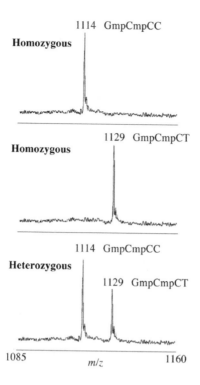

Figure 8.7. Representative MALDI-TOF positive ion mass spectra for genotyping of an SNP on the human β-2 adrenergic receptor using the modified GOOD assay mp = methylphosphonate. The spectra show DNA homozygous for C and T as well as heterozygous DNA (adapted from Sauer et al. Nucleic Acids Research 2002).

Overview

The rapid growth of high throughput chemistry has created a need for faster, more accurate, and more sensitive analytical techniques capable of large-scale screening. Numerous improvements in speed, sensitivity and accuracy, together with innovations in both automation and quantitation place mass spectrometry among the most powerful analytical techniques available today. There are now many analyzer options for high throughput analysis of compounds, as well as multiple ionization techniques that have a much greater range of compatible compounds than were available even five years ago. Quantitative ESI-MS has been shown to be an effective assay for the identification of inhibitor activity in a combinatorial library, namely potent nucleotide inhibitors of a galactosyltransferase. Clearly, this approach can be applied to a variety of different reaction systems. MALDI-based assays are versatile tools for the high-throughput genotyping of SNPs and other point mutations in human DNA. Overall, the strength of mass spectrometry lies in such versatility, making it a powerful analytical technique with which to characterize the diversity of compounds found in modern high throughput chemistry.

Questions

- What is MUX?

- Why can one bad sample ruin an entire run?

- Why use mass spectrometry for enzyme inhibitor screening?

- Why use mass spectrometry for single-nucleotide polymorphisms screening?

- Why are surfaced based mass spectrometry approaches like MALDI and DIOS so much faster than API techniques?

Useful References

Hegy G, Gorlach E, Richmond R, Bitsch F. *High throughput electrospray mass spectrometry of combinatorial chemistry racks with automated contamination surveillance and results reporting*. Rapid Commun. Mass Spectrom. **1996**, 10, 1894-1900.

Wu J, Shuichi T, Wong C-H, Siuzdak G. *Quantitative electrospray mass spectrometry for the rapid assay of enzyme inhibitors*. Chemistry and Biology. **1997**, 4, 653-657.

Wu J, Chatman K, Harris K, Siuzdak G. *An automated MALDI mass spectrometry approach for optimizing cyclosporin extraction and quantitation*. Anal. Chem. **1997**, 69, 3767-3771.

Ross P, Hall L, Smirnov I, Haff L. *High level multiplex genotyping by MALDI-TOF mass spectrometry*. Nat. Biotechnol. **1998**, 16:13, 1347-51.

Ventura MC, Farrell WP, Aurigemma CA, Greig MJ. *Packed column supercritical fluid chromatography/mass spectrometry for high-throughput analysis.* Part 2. Anal. Chem. **1999**, 71, 4223-4231.

Berger TA, Fogelman K, Staats T, Bente P, Crocket I, Farrell W, Osonubi M. *The development of a semi-preparatory scale supercritical-fluid chromatograph for high-throughput purification of 'combi-chem' libraries.* .J. Biochem. Biophys. Methods. **2000**, 43:1-3, 87-111.

Bayliss MK, Little D, Mallett DN, Plumb RS. *Parallel ultra-high flow rate liquid chromatography with mass spectrometric detection using a multiplex electrospray source for direct, sensitive determination of pharmaceuticals in plasma at extremely high throughput.* Rapid. Commun. Mass. Spectrom. **2000**, 14, 21, 2039-45.

Buetow KH, Edmonson M, MacDonald R, et. al. *High-throughput development and characterization of a genome wide collection of gene-based single nucleotide polymorphism markers by chip-based matrix-assisted laser desorption/ionization time-of-flight mass spectrometry.* Proc. Natl. Acad. Sci. USA. **2001**, 98, 581-584.

Hoke SH, Tomlinson II JA, Bolden RD, Morand KL, Pinkston JD, Wehmeyer KR. *Increasing bioanalytical throughput using pcSFC-MS/MS: 10 minutes per 96-well plate.* Anal. Chem. **2001**, 73, 3083-3088.

Lee H, Griffin TJ, Gygi SP, Rist B, Aebersold R. *Development of a multiplexed microcapillary liquid chromatography system for high-throughput proteome analysis.* Analyt. Chem. **2002**, 74, 17, 4353-60.

Sascha Sauer S. Gelfand DH, Boussicault F, Bauer K, Reichert F, Gut IG. *Facile method for automated genotyping of single nucleotide polymorphisms by mass spectrometry* Nucleic Acids Research, **2002**, 30:5 e22.

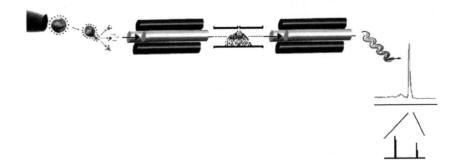

Chapter 9

Pharmacokinetics

... drowning in information and starving for knowledge.
— Rutherford D. Rogers

Perspective

Pharmacokinetics is the study of the absorption, distribution, metabolism, and excretion (ADME) of drugs. The respective rates of these actions are of fundamental importance in determining a drug's effect on the organism to which it is administered. Pharmacokinetic studies with mass spectrometry can provide quantitative information about a compound's half-life in the body and how quickly it is metabolized or excreted. These studies are also used to determine drug distribution, partitioning within an organism, and a drug dosing régime. The latter is important in determining a drug's therapeutic range, which is a balance between the concentration required for positive therapeutic effect versus higher doses which may have toxicological effects. Finally, pharmacokinetics is used to investigate drug dosing with regards to administration factors of age, gender, ethnicity, concomitant drugs, or diseases.

The application of mass spectrometry to pharmacokinetics has revolutionized the drug industry and plays a careful role in the discovery process. The initial mass spectrometric technique used in pharmacokinetics, gas chromatography/mass spectrometry, was limited to molecules that were either volatile or could be made thermally stable by pre-column derivatization.

Liquid chromatography coupled with soft ESI or APCI with triple quadrupole mass analysis (**Figure 9.1**) is the primary tool in pharmacokinetic studies. This is because LC/MS and LC MS/MS are capable of simultaneously generating molecular weight, structural information, and accurate quantitative information regarding the metabolism of a drug. This is highly significant given that recently approved drugs are more potent and therefore administered at concentrations that are difficult to detect with traditional techniques. Mass spectrometry has quite literally revolutionized bioanalytical analysis in the drug discovery and development process, reducing the method development time to a few days or less and providing limits of quantitation of less than 1 nanogram/mL from complex matrices such as plasma, serum, urine, and cellular media.

Multiple reaction monitoring (MRM) is one of the most important tools for acquiring pharmacokinetic data using a triple quadrupole mass spectrometer (**Figure 9.1**). MRM works by simultaneously monitoring for multiple precursor ions by quickly scanning different *m/z* values that correspond to (for example) a drug and its metabolite. Since it is possible that other molecules may have the same mass, an additional confirmation step is performed with MRM where the identity of the precursor ion is confirmed by also monitoring for fragments specific to that precursor ion.

Multiple Reaction Monitoring (MRM) with a triple quadrupole

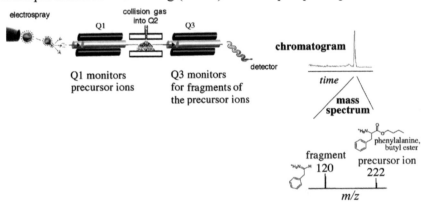

Figure 9.1. Multiple reaction monitoring (MRM) is a valuable tool in the quantitation of drugs and their metabolites. This example is the butyl ester of an amino acid where *m/z* 222 is the precursor [phenylalanine + H]+ and the fragment ion *m/z* 120.

Sample Collection and Extraction

To measure levels of administered drugs and/or metabolites, biological samples such as urine and plasma are typically collected from human patients or laboratory animals. Interfering materials can be removed from these samples and the drug and/or its metabolites of interest can be concentrated prior to analysis using one of several techniques, including protein precipitation, solid phase extraction, liquid-liquid extraction, solid-liquid extraction or acid-base extraction. Liquid-liquid extractions and protein precipitation can be performed in 96-well plates using modern robotic liquid-handling systems, reducing sample preparation times by 3-fold. Solid-liquid extraction using 96-well diatomaceous earth plates has the advantage of providing clean extracts, reduced sample preparation time, and increased sample throughput. Once the compound(s) of interest have been extracted, quantitative measurements of the drug's lifetime in the biofluid can be established by LC/MS (**Figure 9.2**).

Extracted ion chromatogram
from an LC ESI-MS run of a drug

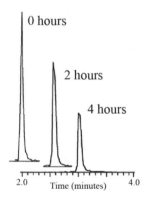

Figure 9.2. LC/MS of an extracted drug at different time points after incubation or dosing.

High Throughput Screening Techniques in Pharmacokinetics

Improvements in the mass spectrometer's ionization source, its overall accuracy, and the implementation of computer-controlled automation have increased the efficiency of screening potential drug molecules for efficacy. Faster production of pure compound libraries, which feed these high throughput screens, has increased the hit rate on biological targets. This corresponding increase in hits has introduced more lead compounds into the discovery process. Historically, ADME assays were performed during the development stage of drug discovery. Recently, more and more of these assays have become a routine part of an initial screening regimen, designed to advance only those compounds with a high likelihood of becoming orally delivered drugs.

Flow injection analysis coupled with ESI or APCI eliminates the chromatographic column and therefore reduces the turnaround time for screening large numbers of samples. However, although fast, the absence of chromatographic separation in this method means that little can be gleaned regarding compound purity and signal suppression may arise due to interference in the sample. For these reasons LC/MS has become a relatively high throughput screening tool for potential drug candidates. Although the overall analyses are slower than with flow injection analysis, chromatographic separation is often required for both purity assessment as well as quantitative measurements. To increase throughput, the simultaneous use of multiple columns can help compensate for longer runtimes by allowing samples to be run in parallel. Multiple-column systems can also be coupled to a multiplexed ionization source (MUX^{TM}), which enables 4 or 8 streams (**Figure 9.3**) to be sprayed into the mass spectrometer, thereby performing the LC/MS analysis 4 to 8 times faster than with a single sprayer. Ultimately, this approach does sacrifice accuracy for speed since each channel is being monitored at proportionally smaller time periods.

ESI MUX

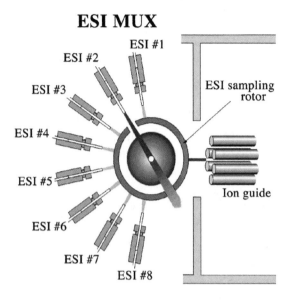

Figure 9.3. An electrospray ionization (ESI) MUX setup for high throughput pharmacokinetics studies.

Cassette-accelerated screening of several drug compounds using 96-well plate formats combined with LC/MS has also reduced sample preparation time and increased compound throughput. Alternatively, ultrafast LC/MS methods can be applied. These involve gradient separations on narrow bore, short HPLC columns and high flow rates that are performed in less than 2 minutes while still maintaining chromatographic integrity. These ultrafast techniques have the advantage of simplicity over multiplexing, for which both the equipment and method validation is more complicated.

Metabolite identification and quantitation

In the drug discovery process, early metabolite identification is needed for patient protection against toxicity and to determine if any metabolites are related to known drugs or have inherent activity against the therapeutic target or other targets. This, in turn, can accelerate the selection of potential clinical candidates and allow early rejection of candidates that would otherwise require critical resources to develop. For compounds that are screened for their metabolic stability, metabolite identification can yield important feedback information for chemists who can then avoid synthesizing structures that are rapidly turned over. The use of triple quadrupole and ion trap instruments for LC/MS/MS represents a powerful combination to investigate various biotransformations by allowing multiple reaction monitoring (MRM), neutral loss, precursor ion scanning, and MS^n for the identification of drug metabolites.

Commonly occurring metabolites are produced as a result of keto-formation (M+14), hydroxylation (M+16), dihydroxylation (M+32) and glucuronidation (M+176), among others. For quantitation of specific metabolites, to determine enzyme kinetics, and for MRM, a triple quadrupole mass spectrometer is most commonly used (**Figure 9.1**).

When the drug metabolite is not known, a variety of experiments can be performed to deduce its structure (**Figure 9.4 and 9.5**). ESI-FTMS technology for accurate mass determination, together with tandem mass measurements for structural characterization using collision induced dissociation. However, despite the important information gleaned from mass spectrometry, the lack of comprehensive mass spectral libraries often limits the identification of molecules using this data alone. Ultimately, the combination of many technologies will be required to identify unknown metabolites in biofluids. Other technologies that can be utilized in metabolite identification are high sensitivity capillary NMR experiments, which provide metabolite structure characterization down to low microgram level. In addition, chemical modification experiments also offer structural information.

A recent example of this approach to metabolite profiling and characterization allowed for the identification of a completely novel set of molecules as taurine-conjugated fatty acids. A three step method was used to identify these metabolites, 1) ultra-high accuracy FTMS mass measurements, 2) high accuracy tandem mass analysis using a Q-TOF, and 3) chemical synthesis of potential candidates based on the results of the 1) and 2). An example of the data is shown in **Figure 9.5**. Accurate mass measurements of the m/z 446 metabolite by ESI-FTMS provided an exact mass of 446.3310, which corresponded to a molecular formula of

$C_{24}H_{48}NO_4S$. The theoretical and experimental isotope patterns for $C_{24}H_{48}NO_4S$ overlaid well, including the splitting pattern of the M + 2 isotope caused by differences in the mass between two ^{13}C isotopes and one ^{34}S isotope. MS/MS analyses of the natural and synthetic metabolites using a Q-TOF instrument led to their structural assignments as N-acyl taurines.

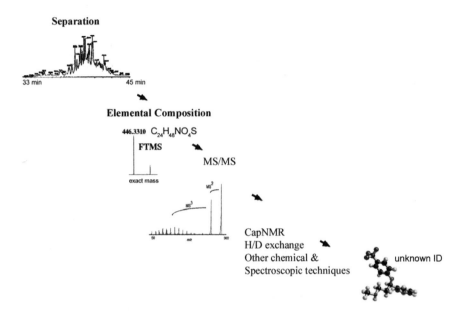

Figure 9.4. Diagrammatic representation of an approach to profiling and characterizing metabolites. Characterization can be facilitated through accurate mass measurements and tandem mass spectral data. Other spectroscopic techniques, such as NMR are very useful for the complete identification of unknown compounds.

FTMS high resolution analysis

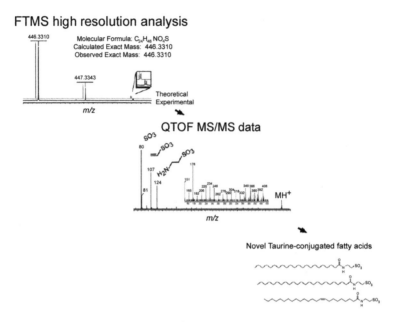

Figure 9.5. An example of the chemical characterization of a previously unknown and unidentified metabolites, the N-acyl taurines. Analysis of the m/z 446 metabolite by ESI-FTMS provided an exact mass of 446.3310, corresponding to a molecular formula of $C_{24}H_{48}NO_4S$. The calculated isotope pattern for $C_{24}H_{48}NO_4S$ overlaid well with the experimental spectrum, including the splitting pattern of the M + 2 isotope (inset) caused by differences in the mass between two ^{13}C isotopes and one ^{34}S isotope. MS/MS data of an N-acyl taurine obtained on a Q-TOF instrument generated prominent fragments corresponding to taurine (124), vinylsulfonic acid (107), and sulfur trioxide (80), as well as a pattern of progressive loss of 14 mass units from m/z 150-430 indicative of a fatty acyl chain. Structures of the three main N-acyl taurines identified. (adapted from Saghatelian, et.al., Biochemistry, 2004)

LC-TOF/MS

The use of LC-API-MS/MS in metabolite recognition and structure elucidation studies often involves extensive method development. Due to the scarcity of supporting qualitative information, this can extend the time of the drug discovery process. The application of TOF to these studies can provide additional data to that obtained with quadrupole or quadrupole ion trap instruments, as full scan TOF spectra can be collected with greater sensitivity and speed. TOF instruments retain, separate, and detect a larger percentage of the ions (5-50% because they simultaneously analyze all ions. Because of the scanning nature of quadrupole analyzers, only ions of specified m/z are allowed to reach the detector. TOF instruments, however, cannot yet match the signal-to-noise ratios achieved in tandem quadrupole mass spectrometers.

Supercritical Fluid Chromatography Mass Spectrometry (SFC-MS)

In recent years, supercritical fluid chromatography has grown in popularity as a complementary technique to liquid chromatography for the separation of compound libraries. SFC is a normal phase chromatographic technique that has high chromatographic efficiency and selectivity and therefore allows for short run times (typically under 1 minute). The excellent mass transfer of SFC allows for higher flow rates (mobile phase linear velocities) and the use of longer columns without increased back pressure. Another advantage is that since carbon dioxide is the preferred bulk eluent, organic solvent consumption and waste is reduced, which is particularly useful for large-scale operations. SFC has demonstrated high resolution, speed, and efficiency when screening pharmaceutical compound libraries and is currently being developed for pharmacokinetics studies.

Quantitation using internal or external standards

The most common calibration method used for pharmacokinetic studies is "internal standardization" whereby a precise quantity of reference material is "spiked" into a sample. A requirement needed for internal standards is that their physicochemical characteristics should be identical or similar to those of the analyte of interest during the measurement. Traditionally, stable isotope labeled compounds and structural homologs or analogs have been used as internal standards. When an internal standard is used, quantitation is typically based on a ratio of the analyte to the internal standard, multiplied by the known concentration of the internal standard (**Figure 9.6**). Generally, the more closely the final concentration of the reference material is to the analyte, the more reliable are the results.

Quantitative LC/MS Analysis

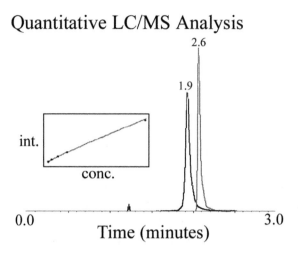

Figure 9.6. Quantitation of lidocaine (1.9 min) using LC/MS with an internal standard (2.6 min) present for improved quantitation.

This simple method of quantitation is acceptable if the linearity of the method, that is the response factor or intensity-of-signal per unit concentration, has been demonstrated to be constant over the concentration range of both the analyte and internal standard. While it is often challenging to arrive at an appropriate internal standard, the benefit of this standardization technique is that the internal standard can be added to a sample early in the analysis and prior to sample preparation. Therefore, if the internal standard and analyte have similar characteristics, any loss of the analyte during sample preparation will be reflected by a concomitant loss of internal standard but the ratio of their concentrations will still reflect the original quantity of the analyte. The benefits also extend to the analytical system, where the absence of internal standard peaks during a run can lead to accelerated identification of injector errors or other system failures.

Calibration of a method using an external standard has the benefit of allowing use of authentic reference material where the reference material is used to generate an external calibration curve for the batch of samples. The frequency of recalibration of the system depends on the stability of the analytical methods; on an LC-

MS/MS quadrupole system, it can be as frequent as twice daily. In general, "system-suitability standards" or "QC/QA controls" are also interspersed in the sample batch during analysis. These controls serve as internal process controls that qualify the analytical testing throughout the entire process.

Mass Spectrometry in Pharmacokinetic Studies

Pharmacokinetic studies are *in vivo* studies whereby an animal is dosed with a compound whose levels and/or its metabolites are measured at extended time intervals (i.e., over a 24-hour period for caffeine, **Figure 9.7**). Pharmacokinetic studies are conducted using a variety of administration routes, such as oral, subcutaneous intraperitoneal, intravenal, or by intramuscular injection. These studies provide information about the bioavailability of a drug, or the concentration of a drug in the bloodstream from the time when it is dosed until the time it is either metabolized or cleared from the body. This data is then used in the drug discovery process to enable the determination of toxic levels, a therapeutic range, a dosing regimen, and to establish proper animal models for development.

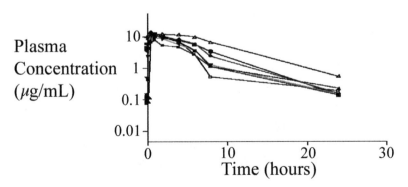

Figure 9.7. To investigate the pharmacokinetics of caffeine in 7 rats, plasma levels were measured over 24 hours. The drug was dosed at the portal vein and the uptake. The gradual clearance of the drug could then be seen over time.

Pharmacokinetic studies are also performed in humans as a necessary part of drug development. They are most often associated with early phase clinical trials (Phase I) where a very small number of patients are individually studied for drug tolerance. For example, in one study group 20 healthy male volunteers were dosed with one of two oral formulations of 20/12.5 mg tablets of enalapril/hydrochlorothiazide and multiple plasma samples were collected over the following 96 hours. Drug bioavailability was evaluated on the basis of plasma concentrations of enalapril and its main active metabolites, enalaprilat and hydrochlorothiazide, by assaying plasma samples for these three compounds using LC/MS.

Mass Spectrometry in Mass Balance Studies

When investigating the elimination of an administered drug, it is necessary to identify and account for the majority of the drug and its metabolites. This is achieved through mass balance studies, most frequently by administering the drug containing a radioactive isotope label such as ^{14}C or ^{3}H, followed by liquid scintillation counting as well as direct or indirect radioactive monitoring of materials subjected to HPLC fractionation. However, the possibility of high radiation exposure (when handling drugs with long half-lives) and the difficulty of tracing a radiolabeled physiological dose preclude the use of radiolabels in human volunteers. In addition, there are environmental issues relating to radioactive material disposal.

To circumvent these problems, a number of alternative mass spectrometry-based analytical methods have been devised, all with the intent of increasing the sensitivity of the method to reduce the level of radioactive material needed. For instance, isotope-labeling combined with accelerator mass spectrometry (AMS), chemical reaction interface-mass spectrometry (CRIMS), and continuous flow-isotope ratio mass spectrometry (CF-IRMS) have emerged as alternatives to the more traditional techniques.

In the ultrasensitive technique of AMS, the drug is labeled with either ^{3}H or ^{13}C and the samples are converted into solid forms amenable to AMS. The wide dynamic range of AMS allows for a 12-fold lower concentration limit of detection than liquid scintillation counting, with better accuracy and precision and therefore a negligible radiological dose requirement for distribution and mass balance studies (<10 nCi). However, at present there are limitations to this technique, including instrument size (typically 4.5m x 6m) and lack of interface between the HPLC and AMS, resulting in the need to collect samples in an off-line fashion.

HPLC combined with chemical reaction interface-mass spectrometry (HPLC/CRIMS) can be used to detect stable isotope enriched macromolecules. Analytes are first eluted from an HPLC and then dissociated in a microwave reaction chamber. The dissociated analytes are oxidized using SO_2 and the resulting small molecules are detected using a mass spectrometer. The stable isotope-labeled analyte can be distinguished from the matrix carbon by monitoring for the enrichment of $^{13}CO_2$.

Continuous flow-isotope ratio mass spectrometry has been used successfully for the analysis of $^{15}N^{13}C_2$ acetaminophen in urine, feces and bile from humans in mass balance studies. Samples are dried and then converted into a gas in an elemental analyzer. The combustion products, in this case ^{15}N and $^{13}CO_2$, are transferred to a gas chromatograph isotope ratio-mass spectrometer via a continuous stream of helium.

Recently, the combination of LC/MS and chemiluminescent-nitrogen detection (CLND) has been used to study pharmacokinetic properties and the measurement of mass balance *in vivo*. This method was used as an alternative to studies using a radiolabeled tracer, with the only requirement for quantitation being the presence of nitrogen in the parent compound and the metabolites.

Improvements in Protein Therapeutics

Mass spectrometry also plays an important role in both the discovery and characterization of biotherapeutic agents. The high demand to discover new drugs and to identify new therapeutic targets has led researchers to focus on cellular proteins. This has been greatly facilitated by the significant advances of mass spectrometry in the field of proteomics. Mass spectrometric techniques, established in the drug discovery arena, including new combinations of mass analyzers, improved ion sources, and miniaturization of on-line sample methods, are now applied to all parts of drug discovery and development. The role of mass spectrometry in proteomics is constantly expanding. The most commonly used techniques in this area are LC/ESI-MS^2 and MALDI-TOF (**Figure 9.8**), which can be used to characterize protein expression and to identify protein variants and post-translational modifications.

Protein Analysis with Mass Spectrometry

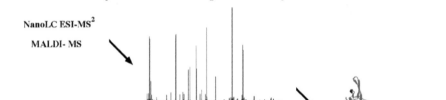

Figure 9.8. Mass spectrometry in proteomics is facilitating the discovery of new protein drugs, which is providing new challenges for pharmacokinetics.

A major consideration and challenge in the development of biopharmaceuticals remains the determination of the distribution and elimination of these drugs. Previously, drugs had a natural, biological base and were either direct hormone replacements (such as insulin or human growth factor), vaccines, or antisera. The administration of these biologicals was often based on arbitrary units of activity, such as international units, which in turn were based on an international reference standard. There was little concern with the distribution and metabolism of these biologically-based products. This has changed with the evolution of biopharmaceuticals, as seen with the widespread development of monoclonal antibodies (native or conjugant), fusion proteins, recombinant enzymes, soluble receptors, etc. The latest trend in this area is the development of generic classes of biologicals; this requires defining and grouping these products based on their physical and chemical properties rather than on their apparent activity and manufacturing procedures. The use of LC/MS for both distribution and mass balance studies of these molecules will follow the same principles as those for traditional drugs. Marketing of these new protein drugs will have the additional challenges of accounting for heterogeneity of the drug candidate, unfamiliar metabolic transformations, and the need to determine what role immunological interaction will have on drug potency and elimination.

Overview

A major driving force in the development of mass spectrometry is its utility in the discovery and development of drugs in the pharmaceutical industry. With the increased demand for ADME data earlier in the drug discovery process, the sensitivity and versatility of mass spectrometry has proven it to be a reliable and invaluable tool in the pharmacology laboratory. Improved chromatographic techniques coupled with advances in mass analysis technology have meant that biodistribution and elimination studies can now be developed and implemented in a matter of days rather than weeks or months. Widespread use of electrospray ionization and atmospheric pressure chemical ionization have contributed to ease of use in acquisition of high quality quantitative data necessary for pharmacokinetic studies.

Questions

- What is ADME?

- Why is mass spectrometry so useful for pharmacokinetics studies?

- Where in pharmacokinetics does mass accuracy have the most benefit?

- Where in pharmacokinetics does quantitative accuracy have the most benefit?

- Why does SFC-MS have such great potential in pharmacokinetics?

- What are some of the challenges that face pharmacokinetics in the future?

Useful References

Browne TR, Szabo GK, Ajami A, Browne DG. *Performance of human mass balance studies with stable isotope-labeled drug and continuous flow-isotope ratio mass spectrometry: a progress report.* J. Clin. Pharmacol. **1998**, 38:4, 309-14.

Ventura MC, Farrell WP, Aurigemma CM, Greig MJ. *Packed column supercritical fluid chromatography/mass spectrometry for high-throughput analysis.* Anal. Chem. **1999**, 71, 2410-2416.

Zhang N, Fountain ST, H Bi, Rossi DT. *Quantification and rapid metabolite identification in drug discovery using API Time-of-Flight LC/MS.* Analyt. Chem. **2000**, 72, 800-806.

O'Connor DO, Clarke DE, Morrison D, Watt AP. *Determination of drug concentrations in plasma by a highly automated, generic and flexible protein precipitation and liquid chromatography/tandem mass spectrometry method applicable to the drug discovery environment.* J. Med Chem. **2002**, 37, 1385-1401.

Korfmacher WA, Cox KA, Ng KJ, Veals J, Hsieh Y, Wainhaus S, Broske L, Prelusky D, Nomeir A, White RE. *Cassette-accelerated rapid rat screen: a systematic procedure for the dosing and liquid chromatography/ atmospheric pressure ionization tandem mass spectrometric analysis of new chemical entities as part of new drug discovery.* Rapid Commun. Mass Spectrom. **2002**, 37, 1385-1401.

Tiller PR & Romanyshyn LA. *Liquid chromatography/tandem mass spectrometric quantification with metabolic screening as a strategy to enhance the early drug discovery process.* Rapid Commun. Mass Spectrom. **2002**, 16, 1225-1231.

Saghatelian A, Trauger SA, Want E, Hawkins G, Siuzdak G, Cravatt BF. *Assignment of Endogenous Substrates to Enzyme by Global Metabolite Profiling.* Biochemistry, **2004**, 43, p.14332-14339.

Chapter 10

Mass Spectrometry in Action

What would you attempt to do if you knew you
would not fail? - Robert Schuller

Perspective

Throughout this book I've tried to outline many of the
capabilities that mass spectrometry can offer. In this chapter the focus
instead turns to significant biochemical problems and how mass
spectrometry is being used to deal with and solve them. Specifically,
snapshots are provided of the rapidly growing field of metabolite
profiling, the use of mass spectrometry (instead of fluorescence) for
monitoring enzyme catalysis, and the role of ethanol in testosterone
biosynthesis. I will also show an example of how mass spectrometry has
been used to correlate protein modifications with disease and drug
intake, its use in examining the proteomics of the malaria organism, and
(my favorite topic) in the mass measurement of an intact virus.

Endogenous Metabolite Profiling: Disease Diagnosis

Donald H. Chace. *Mass Spectrometry in the Clinical Laboratory.* Chem. Rev. **2001**, 101,
p.445-477.

Shen Z, Go EP, Gamez A, Apon JV, Fokin V, Greig M, Ventura M, Crowell JE, Blixt O,
Paulson JC, Stevens R, Finn MG, Siuzdak G. *A Mass Spectrometry Plate Reader:
Monitoring Enzyme and Inhibitor Activity with Desorption/Ionization on Silicon (DIOS)
Mass Spectrometry.* ChemBioChem, **2004**, 5, p.921-927.

Natural products isolated from organisms such as plants and
marine animals have long been examined for unique biological activity,
yielding numerous clinically active compounds. For example, penicillin

was originally identified from bread molds and the chemotherapy agent, taxol, from the ewe tree. However, surprisingly few of the myriad small biomolecules that make up endogenous metabolites have been characterized. An example of our limited knowledge can be demonstrated from a mass profile obtained by liquid chromatography/ mass spectrometry (LC/MS) of a simple human tear, revealing hundreds of small, unidentified biomolecules (**Figure 10.1**).

LC ESI-MS (Positive)

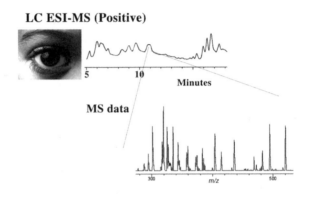

Figure 10.1. The LC ESI-MS ion chromatogram and MS data from a human tear. As shown, numerous ions were observed from a relatively small region of the LC run.

The numerous endogenous metabolites that exist in humans have motivated their examination using mass spectrometry coupled with separation techniques such as liquid chromatography. The primary purpose of these studies is to identify new molecules for disease diagnosis. Historically, GC/MS has been widely used in disease diagnosis, including disorders of the metabolism of amino acids (**Figure 10.2**), thyroid hormones, bile acids, steroids, organic acids and fatty acids, with 20-30 disorders of the latter alone having been characterized. However, due to the many limitations of GC/MS, LC/MS has become a more popular choice for these analysis methods over immunological, fluorometric and biological techniques. Today over thirty five diseases in newborns (**Figure 10.2**), including the screening for phenylketonuria (PKU), are monitored directly using ESI-MS.

PKU is one of the metabolite diseases, analyzed in newborn baby screens, where the transformation of phenylalanine to tyrosine is monitored using ESI-MS. The absence of the enzyme phenylalanine hydrolase results in the lack of the formation of tyrosine (**Figure 10.3**) and the quantitative analysis of the amino acids in newborn blood samples allows for the prediction of disease states.

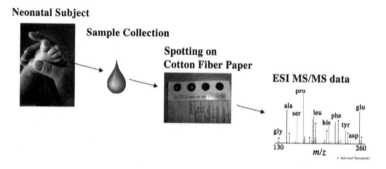

Figure 10.2. Electrospray ionization mass spectrometry is the basis of neonatal screening of blood samples that allows for the identification of thirty-five different diseases. (Courtesy of Don Chace)

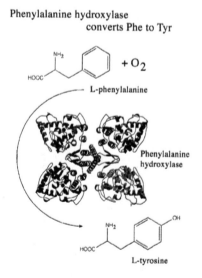

Figure 10.3. The absence of phenylalanine hydroxylase (PheOH), which converts phenylalanine to tyrosine, results in the metabolite disease known as phenylketourea (PKU). We have developed DIOS-MS as platform to screen enzyme alternatives as potential drugs.

Monitoring Enzyme Catalysis

Wu J, Takayama S, Wong CH, Siuzdak G. *Quantitative Electrospray Mass Spectrometry for the Rapid Assay of Enzyme Inhibitors.* Chemistry & Biology, **1997**, 4:9, 653-657.

Thomas JJ, Shen Z, Crowell JE, Finn MG, Siuzdak G. *Desorption/Ionization on Silicon (DIOS): A Diverse Mass Spectrometry Platform for Protein Characterization.* Proceedings of the National Academy of Sciences, **2001**, 98, 4932-4937

As demonstrated in the previous section, an important application of mass spectrometry is screening enzyme activity (**Figure 10.4**). In addition to serving as a screen for neonatal diseases, activity screens are an important tool for monitoring drugs that act as enzyme inhibitors. Mass spectrometry can also be used to identify novel enzymes that are effective for a specific substrate. Potential inhibitors as well as enzyme libraries can be rapidly screened for activity via the analysis of the substrate and product in the presence of the entire enzymatic mixture (enzyme, substrate, inhibitor, product, and internal standard). Since either substrate or product formation can be quantitatively monitored, the effectiveness of the inhibitor or enzyme can be readily determined.

Enzyme Reaction

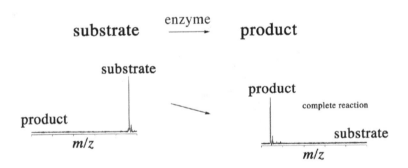

substrate $\xrightarrow{\text{enzyme}}$ product

Figure 10.4. Enzymatic reactions can be monitored with mass spectrometry. In this example, the ratio of product to substrate or the appearance of either product or substrate can be used to determine if an enzyme is active.

Other assays used for monitoring enzyme activity include radiolabelling, NMR, fluorimetry, spectrophotometry, affinity capillary electrophoresis, and surface plasmon resonance. Many of these assays require a chromophore or radiolabelling which can affect enzyme activity, require significant time to develop, and involve biohazards. The value of mass spectrometry lies in its simplicity; if the substrate or product is ionizable the assay requires minimal effort to complete (**Figure 10.4**).

Fluorescent plate readers are typically used for inhibitor screening and are not without their own limitations. These include:

False positives (inhibitors that fluoresce)

False negatives (inhibitors that quench fluorescence)

Development of a fluorescent assay protocol (weeks to months)

Mass spectrometry offers high-throughput analyses of small molecule inhibitors as well as an accurate quantitative enzyme assay that does not require a chromophore or radiolabelling. Mass spectral data can currently be acquired at a rate of one sample per 5 seconds where the analysis rate is limited by instrument hardware (data acquisition system and translation platform) rather than any inherent limitation in mass spectrometry methodology. It is anticipated that instrumentation improvements such as faster electrospray ionization source analysis or faster MALDI/DIOS x-y translation motors, a redesign of the software and a faster digitizing scope could provide for at least a 5-fold enhancement in acquisition rate to greater than one sample per second (~100,000 samples per day). With such improvements, mass spectrometry will be of great use as an analytical tool in numerous high-throughput applications, particularly in the discovery of novel enzyme inhibitors. The utility of mass spectrometry in proteomics is also evident because of the ease with which assays can be developed for different enzymes. Since the only prerequisite for the mass spectrometry is an ionizable substrate (or product), it can be broadly applied to virtually any enzyme for monitoring inhibition or characterizing activity of novel enzymes.

Key advantages of mass spectrometry as a primary screen in drug discovery is that it allows the identification of new inhibitors (or even novel enzymes), no false positives or false negatives, it is accurate, sensitive, has no biohazards and the assay development is simple.

Testosterone Biosynthesis from Ethanol

Alomary, Vallée, O'Dell, Koob, Purdy, Fitzgerald. *Acutely-administered Ethanol Participates in Testosterone Synthesis and Increases Testosterone in Rat Brain.* Alcohol Clin. Exp. Res. **2003**, 27, 38-43.

The interaction of ethanol and testosterone has long been of interest, largely because of the effect alcohol has on aggression and sexual behavior. However, little effort has been exerted to examine the role of ethanol on testosterone concentrations in the brain and in biofluids. A recent study took advantage of high sensitivity of selected ion monitoring (SIM) experiments with negative chemical ionization GC/MS and a deuterated ethanol (1,1-dideuteroethanol) standard to determine if ethanol could be directly linked to testosterone synthesis.

Androstenedione   [17 α-d₁]-Testosterone

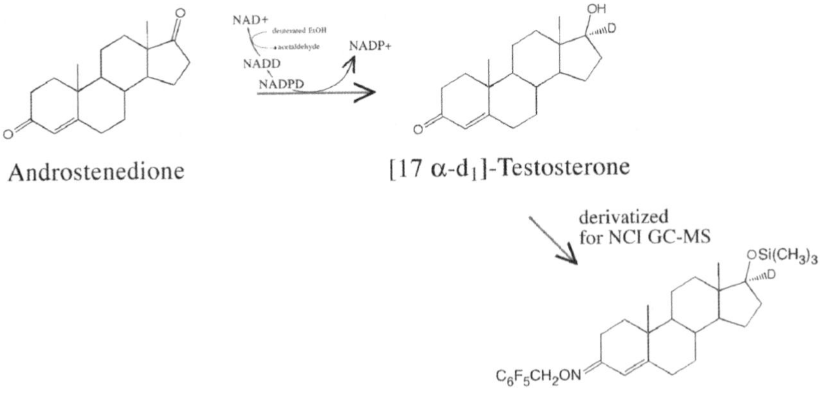

Figure 10.6. Conversion of androstenedione to testosterone through NADPH. NADPH is affected by the presence of ethanol as demonstrated by the conversion of NADPH to NADPD resulting in deuterated testosterone. The deuterated ethanol used in these studies was 1,1-dideuteroethanol ([1,1-²H2]-ethanol).

In a typical experiment, testosterone levels were monitored after alcohol administration to observe changes in concentration. Further, the deuterated analog of testosterone was monitored to determine if ethanol played a role in its biosynthesis. It was found that the level of total testosterone increased fourfold in the frontal cortex and threefold in the plasma of male rats upon ethanol administration. The observation of deuterium-labeled testosterone in the brain and in plasma following [1,1-2H2]-ethanol showed that ethanol oxidation (**Figures 10.6 & 10.7**) is directly linked to testosterone biosynthesis and that the deuterium-labeled testosterone is present in the central nervous system. These observations correlate well with the behavioral changes associated with ethanol consumption.

Negative Chemical Ionization GC/MS

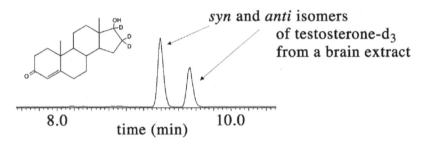

syn and *anti* isomers of testosterone-d₃ from a brain extract

Figure 10.7. Selected ion chromatogram of deuterium labeled testosterone-16,16,17-d3 (*m/z* 538) (pentafluoro-benzyloxyoxime/trimethyl silyl ether derivative), obtained from a 400 mg frontal cortex extract after ethanol administration. The two different retention times represent the separation of the *syn* and *anti* isomers of testosterone observed in the negative chemical ionization GC/MS experiments.

Fibrinogen Heterogeneity and Disease

Henschen-Edman. *Fibrinogen Heterogeneity and Its Relationship to Disease.* Ann. New York Acad. Sci. **2001**, 936, 580-593.

The most significant biological role of the 340 kDa blood plasma protein fibrinogen is related to its ability to form the scaffold of a blood clot and thereby prevent the loss of blood after injury. It is of greatest consequence for the maintenance of health that the capacity of soluble fibrinogen to be converted into insoluble fibrin is meticulously regulated, and that stable fibrin is formed only when and where it is needed. Fibrinogen also plays a role in the physiological and pathological processes related to wound healing, tumor growth, and metastasis as well as defense mechanisms. In order to fulfill its numerous functions, fibrinogen interacts in highly specific ways with large number of other proteins as well as lower molecular weight and cellular components, primarily in the blood stream or blood vessel wall. All functions and interactions are mediated by distinct and specific structural elements of the fibrinogen or fibrin molecule, i.e. the functional sites. They correspond to short amino acid sequences or to regional conformations and may be differentially expressed in fibrinogen, fibrin, and their degradation products.

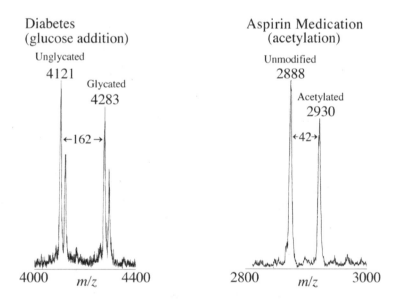

Figure 10.8. MALDI-MS data on fibrinogen fragments corresponding to modifications that occurred either from a diabetes disease (glucose addition) or medication with aspirin (acetylation).

Human fibrinogen is present in the blood of healthy individuals in over a million non-identical forms due to the many combinations of post-translational modifications and genetically polymorphic sites.

Certain combinations have been shown to influence the functional properties and preferentially occur in conjunction with disease. Normal post-translational variants are caused by alternative splicing, modification of certain amino acid residues and proteolysis. Modifications of amino acids include serine phosphorylation, tyrosine sulfation, proline hydroxylation, and asparagines glycosylation. Most types of modification can be detected and often even quantified by MALDI-TOF mass spectrometry. Additional modification may be specifically caused by diseases or drugs and these modifications will typically change the functional properties of fibrinogen. Disease-induced modifications have been observed in patients suffering from diabetes cancer and autoimmune disease as well as in cigarette smokers. Drug-induced modifications have been found to occur after aspirin medication.

Diabetes is one of the important risk factors for cardiovascular disease and at least partly due to the high glucose levels found in patients with insufficiently controlled or controllable insulin treatment. The risk may specifically be related to the resulting fibrinogen modifications. Recent investigations provide strong evidence for the effect of glucose in fibrinogen structure and function. Mass analyses of fragments of fibrinogen that previously had been incubated with glucose often showed the addition of 162 mass units to the original mass of the fragment, a mass difference that is characteristic of glycation of lysine residues (**Figure 10.8**). Corresponding modifications were also found in the blood from diabetic patients. It is expected that some of these modifications correspond to plasmic cleavage sites and that, accordingly, glycation may interfere with proteolytic clot dissolution and therefore make the clot more dangerous.

In another fibrinogen study of cardiovascular disease the beneficial effects of aspirin were investigated. Aspirin is known to acetylate cyclooxygenase of the prostaglandin system and thereby inhibit the procoagulant function of platelets. However, aspirin treatment will also lead to a looser fibrin clot structure making the clot more accessible to proteolytic dissolution. Mass analysis of fragments of fibrinogen incubated with aspirin showed the addition of 42 mass units, characteristic of acetylation of the fibrinogen lysine residues (**Figure 10.**

Complex Protein Complexes: Malaria

A proteomic view of the Plasmodium falciparum life cycle – *as reported by Jason Socrates Bardi*

Florens, Washburn, Raine, Anthony, Grainger, Haynes, Moch, Muster, Sacci, Tabb, Witney, Wolters, Wu, Gardner, Holder, Sinden, Yates, Carucci. Nature. **2002**.

The proteome of the malaria pathogen (Plasmodium falciparum) has been examined in parallel with a six-year, genome-sequencing effort. Where "genomics" maps the DNA sequence and genes in an organism like Plasmodium falciparum, the proteome adds the topographical information to that map by identifying which genes are actually expressed as proteins in the Plasmodium falciparum cells.

2D Liquid Chromatography Tandem Mass Spectrometry

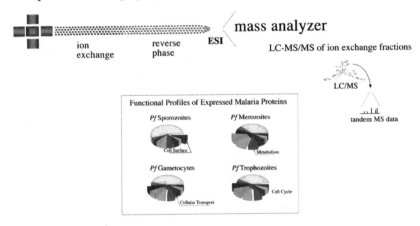

Figure 10.9. Two-dimensional electrospray ionization tandem mass spectrometry experiments were used to identify the Plasmodium falciparum proteins.

The investigators specifically sought to characterize the Plasmodium falciparum proteome at different stages of the organism's lifecycle. Since Plasmodium falciparum has at least ten distinct stages in its lifecycle, it is difficult to determine which proteins are expressed at each distinct stage of the pathogen's lifecycle by examining gene expression. In this study protein characterization was examined during four different stages (sporozoites, merozoites, trophozoites, and gametocytes). The process included taking samples of a single isolate of Plasmodium falciparum and growing three of the four different stages in blood in a way that allowed samples to be purified. The fourth stage, the sporozoites, was hand dissected from mosquito salivary glands.

In purifying the samples, the soluble proteins were separated from the membrane-bound proteins, then digested and analyzed using 2D LC-MS/MS. This approach allowed for the characterization of proteins at different stages of the life cycle. Further, it could be determined which proteins were membrane associated, and which were cytosolic. In this manner, over 2400 different proteins were identified.

Measuring the Mass of Intact Viruses

Siuzdak G, Bothner B, Yeager M, Brugidou C, Fauquet CM, Hoey K, Chang CM. *Mass Spectrometry and Viral Analysis.* Chemistry & Biology. **1996**, 3, 45-48.

Fuerstenau SD, Benner WH, Thomas JJ, Brugidou C, Bothner B, Siuzdak G. *Mass Spectrometry of an Intact Virus.* Angewandte Chemie. **2001**, 40, 542-544.

Bothner B., Siuzdak G. *Electrospray Ionization of a Whole Virus: Analyzing Mass, Structure and Viability.* ChemBioChem, **2004**, 5(3), p.258-260.

There have been significant developments in the past few years in the area of macromolecular analysis of whole viruses and viral capsids. The first was the examination of virus viability following transmission of the whole virus through a mass spectrometer. A brass plate was placed between Q2 and Q3 in a triple quadrupole mass spectrometer where viral particles could be collected (**Figure 10.10**). The plates, when examined using electron microscopy, were found to have intact viral particles. The mass analyzed and collected TMV viral particles were successfully used to infect tobacco plants. The surprising results of these studies demonstrated that intact viruses could be transmitted through the ESI mass spectrometer and that the ionization method was gentle enough for the viruses to retain their virulence.

Given the size of intact viruses, the challenge of measuring them while intact required the development of new technology. The direct measurement of the charge state of very massive ions has been shown using charge detection TOF-MS through image current measurement (Henry Benner at Lawrence Berkeley Laboratories). In time-of-flight charge detection mass spectrometry both the charge and m/z are measured simultaneously providing a direct measure of mass (m). Intact viral particles of the rice yellow mottle virus (RYMV) and the tobacco mosaic virus (TMV) were studied using this approach. The RYMV is an icosahedral non-enveloped virus consisting of a single strand of RNA and multiple copies of a single protein. The RYMV and TMV have theoretical molecular weights of 6.5×10^6 Da and 40.5×10^6 Da, respectively. The mass spectra obtained for TMV is shown in **Figure 10.10**. The measured masses obtained for each virus correlate with the calculated masses.

Mass Spectrometry of an Intact Virus

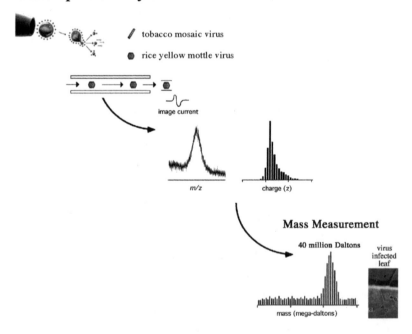

Figure 10.10. Mass spectrum of Tobacco Mosaic Virus (TMV) particles analyzed with an electrospray ionization charge detection time-of-flight mass spectrometer. The known molecular weight of TMV is 40.5×10^6 Daltons, respectively. Inset: An image of a tobacco leaf infected with TMV after electrospray ionization and passage through a mass spectrometer.

Overview

My first book "Mass Spectrometry for Biotechnology" introduced the capabilities of mass spectrometry and some of the major achievements that occurred before 1994. This book is the second edition of "The Expanding Role of Mass Spectrometry in Biotechnology" further expands upon the ongoing improvements and the many new technologies that are now available. Some of the most important ones I've outlined in this chapter including large scale protein characterization, high throughput screening, understanding biochemical synthesis, disease diagnosis and even whole organism mass spectrometry. It is always dangerous to look into the proverbial crystal ball but it is safe to say that mass spectrometry will be even further improved in the near future. These improvements will come through greater accuracy, sensitivity and better quantitative capabilities, opening up even more areas of biochemical research. In particular, I believe mass spectrometry will become the cornerstone of discoveries in disease diagnosis.

Terms and Definitions[1]

Adduction formation. Adduct ion formation is commonly known as cationization or anionization. The noncovalent addition of an ion adduct involves the addition of a cation, (H^+, Na^+, K^+,...) or an anion (Cl^-, I^-, SO_4^-,...), to a molecule. For example, [carbohydrate + $Na]^+$ is a common ion observed for carbohydrates in the positive ion analysis mode. It is also possible to observe neutral noncovalent adducts.

Atmospheric pressure chemical ionization (APCI). A version of chemical ionization performed at atmospheric pressure. The formation of ionized species when gaseous molecules interact with ions (reagent ions) at atmospheric pressure. The reagent ions are formed by a corona discharge of the vaporized solvent introduced into the system.

Atmospheric pressure ionization (API). Ionization technique(s) that occur at atmospheric pressure. Various API ionization techniques include electrospray and atmospheric pressure chemical ionization and API is often used to couple liquid chromotagraphy to mass spectrometry.

Base peak. The most intense peak in the mass spectrum.

Cationization. Cationization involves the noncovalent addition of a positively charged ion to a neutral molecule, resulting in a charged complex that can be observed by mass analysis. While protonation can be thought of as cationization, the term cationization is more commonly used for the addition of a cation adduct (alkali cations) other than a proton. Cationization is a means of producing a stable molecular ion. For example, some molecules that are protonated fragment with little or no formation of the parent molecular ion. This is partially due to the strong binding between a proton and the molecule and thus the transfer of charge to the molecule. The charge transfer can destabilize the molecule and therefore promote fragmentation. Alkali cations effectively "stick" to

---

[1] Some definitions were derived from P. Price (1991), "Standard definitions of terms relating to mass spectrometry," A report from the committee on measurements and standards of the American Society for Mass Spectrometry. *J. Amer. Soc. Mass Spectrom.*, 2, 336-348.

a molecule. Since the binding is not covalent in nature the charge remains localized and a more stable molecular ion is formed.

Chemical ionization. An ionization method where neutral molecules are ionized by ion-molecule reactions.

Collision-induced dissociation (CID). An ion/neutral process wherein the (fast) projectile ion is fragmented as a result of collision with a target neutral species. This process is known as collision-induced dissociation (CID) and/or collision-activated dissociation (CAD). CID (or CAD) is accomplished by conversion, during the collision, of part of the translational energy of the ion to internal energy in the ion. It is accomplished in tandem mass spectrometry by selecting an ion of interest with a mass filter/analyzer and introducing that ion into a collision cell. A collision gas (typically Ar) is also introduced into the collision cell, whereby the selected ion will collide with the neutral atoms within the cell, resulting in fragmentation. The fragments can then be analyzed to obtain a fragment ion (or daughter ion) spectrum.

Cosolvent. A solvent is used to facilitate the solvation of an analyte into a FAB or MALDI matrix system. For example trifluoroacetic acid (TFA) is used to facilitate solvation of some peptides into the FAB matrix, *m*-nitrobenzyl alcohol (NBA).

Cyclotron motion. Cyclic rotation of an ion in a fixed magnetic field.

Dalton. Units of atomic mass (atomic mass units or "amu's") are often referred to as "Daltons" in honor of John Dalton (1766-1844), the first person to look at matter in relation to molecules and atoms.

Derivatization. Chemical alteration of a molecule to increase volatility and thermal stability by reducing intermolecular forces. Derivatization is a preparatory step for the thermal desorption process in electron ionization because it imparts volatility and thermal stability to molecules, making them more amenable to the thermal desorption. Derivatization will generally increase the molecular weight and reduce intermolecular forces by converting polar groups into funtionalities of less polarity.

underivatized carbohydrate

acetylated carbohydrate

The reduction of intermolecular forces, such as hydrogen bonding, is accomplished by removing active hydrogen atoms. For example, acids, amides, or polyalcohols may be acetylated or trimethylsilylated. Electrostatic interactions of zwitterionic amino acids may also be quenched by acetylation and methylation.

Desorption ionization. Desorption ionization is a general term used to encompass the various desorption ionization techniques (e.g., secondary ion MS, fast atom bombardment, plasma desorption, matrix-assisted laser desorption). Desorption ionization generates ions by desorbing analyte from a solid or liquid sample with a nonvolatile particle beam and can be generally described as a method used to desorb and ionize non-volatile solid samples by impact of energetic particles or photon beams.

Distonic ion. Radical ion in which the charge and radical sites are located on different atoms in the molecule.

Electron ionization (also known as Electron Impact). Ionization occurring through molecular interactions with electrons. The electrons, obtained from a heated filment, are accelerated through a certain voltage (typically 70 eV). The electrons transfer this kinetic energy to a molecule to produce ionization. Usually no more than an excess of 5-6 eV above the ionization potential (ionization potentials are usually 8-13 eV) is absorbed. The excess energy often results in significant fragmentation. The reaction $M + e^- \rightarrow M^+ + 2e^-$ is typical of the ionization that occurs in electron ionization. $M + e^- \rightarrow M^-$ also occurs in EI; however, it is usually about 100 times less efficient.

Electron affinity. Enthalpy change for the process $M^- \rightarrow M + e^-$.

Electron capture. Ionization process in which a molecule or atom captures a thermal energy electron typically in a CI source, and generates the molecular radical anion.

Electron capture ionization (ECI). The processes of a molecule capturing an electron to generate an ion.

$$1) \; MX + e^- \rightarrow MX^- \qquad \text{electron capture}$$

$$2) \; MX + e^- \rightarrow M^- + X^- \qquad \text{dissociative electron capture}$$

Electrospray ionization (ESI). Electrospray ionization generates ions by spraying a solution (aqueous or organic solvent) through a charged inlet. Once the solvent is sprayed, its droplets rapidly desolvate through the addition of heat, a stream of gas (air), or both. As the solvent evaporates, ions in the highly charged droplets get ejected. The ions are then electrostatically directed into the mass analyzer. This ion source commonly produces multiply charged ions, making it easy to detect proteins with a quadrupole mass analyzer having a range of m/z 3000.

Exact mass (or **accurate mass measurement** or **high resolution measurements**). Exact mass obtains the mass of an ion within an error of 5 to 30 ppm of the expected mass. These measurements can be used for elemental-composition determination. Requirements of specific journals are listed here, followed by an example.

Journal of the American Chemical Society (JACS): Criteria are ± 5 ppm for mass less than 1000 and unit mass for mass greater than 1000.

Journal of Organic Chemistry (JOC): Criteria are $\rightarrow$ 13 mmu $\pm$ for mass 500-1000 and unit mass for mass greater than 1000.

Compound	Molecular Formula and Exact Mass	Acceptable exact mass range (Da)	
		JACS	JOC
Buckyball	C_{60}=720.0000 Da	719.9964 to 720.0036	719.9840 to 720.0160

Fourier transform ion cyclotron resonance (FTICR) analyzer. A FTICR is an ion trap where ions of all m/z values are excited by applying RF energy over a range of frequencies corresponding to the cyclotron frequencies of the ions. All ions are then detected simultaneously by measuring the current induced on the "detect" electrodes by the confined ions. The mass spectrum is obtained by application of the Fourier transform to the measured signal to extract the cyclotron frequencies of the ions. Once the cyclotron frequencies are known, the m/z values are calculated via the cyclotron equation.

Fragmentation. Fragmentation is a process that occurs when enough energy is concentrated in a bond, causing the vibrating atoms to move apart beyond a bonding distance. In general, fragments resulting from weak bonds are prominent in the mass spectra. Since one vibration takes 10-10 to 10-12 sec there is enough time for a million vibrations to occur before an ion leaves the source. Fragmentation usually occurs in the ionization source.

Gas chromatography/mass spectrometry (GC/MS). A combined technique for mixture analysis in which the separated GC components are passed continuously into the mass spectrometer. Typical ionization sources include EI and CI and typical analyzers include quadrupoles, quadrupole ion traps and time-of-flight.

Ion source. Device used to generate ions.

Ionization and cationization. Ionization of a neutral molecule occurs through the addition or removal of a charged species such as an electron or a proton. The following list represents how mass spectrometers achieve ionization.

> *Alkali cationization.* Accomplished by the addition of an alkali cation. Many compounds are unstable to proton addition, and require alkali cation complexation in order to observe stable molecular ions. Carbohydrates are well known to form stable alkali cationized molecular ions, while their protonated molecular ions are often undetectable.

> *Ammonium cationization.* An alternative to alkali cationization.

Deprotonation. A means of observing ions from acidic compounds. It is accomplished by removing a proton and monitoring them in the negative ion mode.

Electron ejection. The ejection of an electron to form a positive cation. Most ionization techniques will allow you to form this type of ion, but the most common is electron ionization.

Electron capture. Roughly 100 times less likely to occur in electron ionization, therefore it is 100 times less sensitive. The sensitivity is, however, very compound-dependent. For example, pentane will not easily accept an electron while hexafluorobenzene will.

Protonation. Accomplished by the addition of a proton or protons to form a positively charged species. Protonation works well on many polar compounds, proteins and peptides are well known for their ability to obtain a charge through protonation. Protonation may result in destabilization of certain molecules, for example with carbohydrates, in alkali cationization is useful.

Inductively coupled plasma. Plasma ionization method used to ionize solution samples for elemental analysis.

Ion internal energy. Total electronic, vibrational, and rotational energy referenced to ground state of the ion.

Ion trap analyzer. A mass analyzer where ions are confined in a region of space and analyzed.

Paul ion trap. A type of ion trap mass analyzer in which ions are confined in space by means of a three-dimensional, rotationally symmetric quadrupolar electric field. Sorting of ions is performed by changing the field conditions appropriately to destabilize an ion of a particular m/z. The destabilized ion is then detected when it exits the trap and strikes a collection device, e.g. an electron multiplier or conversion dynode.

Penning ion trap. An ion trap mass analyzer that confines ions by placing them in a static magnetic field. Inside the field, the ions are subject to the Lorentz force which causes ions of a particular m/z to cyclotron at a specific frequency (cyclotron frequency).

Liquid secondary ion mass spectrometry (LSIMS). Essentially the same process as fast atom/ion bombardment (FAB), LSIMS orginally derived from secondary ion mass spectrometry (SIMS). SIMS did not incorporate a liquid matrix.

Mass analyzers. Mass analyzers separate ions according to their mass-to-charge ratio (m/z). A description of the more common analyzers are given below.

Magnetic sector analyzer. A direction-focusing device that produces a magnetic field perpendicular to the direction of ion travel. The effect is to bring to a common focus all ions of a given mass-to-charge ratio.

Electrostatic analyzer. A velocity-focusing device for producing an electrostatic field perpendicular to the direction of ion travel (usually used in combination with a magnetic analyzer for mass analysis). The effect is to bring to a common focus all ions that have been accelerated through a given voltage difference.

Quadrupole mass analyzer. A mass filter that creates a quadrupole field with a direct current (dc) component and a radio frequency (rf) component in such a manner as to allow to scan over a selected mass-to-charge range.

Time-of-flight analyzer. A device that measures the flight time of ions over a fixed distance. The time is the same for ions that have been accelerated through the same voltage difference and have the same mass-to-charge ratio.

Ion trap analyzer. A mass-resonance analyzer that produces a three-dimensional rotationally symmetric quadrupole field capable of storing ions at selected mass-to-charge ratios.

Mass measurement. There are three different ways to calculate molecular weight. The way the mass is calculated and how that compares with the observed mass data depends largely on the accuracy and resolution of the mass spectrometer.

> *Average mass*. The mass of an ion calculated from a given empirical formula using the atomic weight (which is an average of the isotopes) for each element, such as
>
> $$C = 12.1115, H = 1.00797, O = 15.9994.$$
>
> *Monoisotopic ion mass*. The mass of an ion calculated from a given empirical formula using the exact mass of the most abundant isotope of each element, such as
>
> $$C = 12.000000, H = 1.007825, O = 15.994915.$$
>
> *Nominal ion mass*. The mass of an ion calculated from a given empirical formula using the integer mass of the most abundant isotope of each element, such as
>
> $$C = 12, H = 1, O = 16.$$

Mass spectrometry. This is the study of mass spectra obtained by using a mass spectrometer. The term "mass spectroscopy" should be avoided, because this implies optical dispersion.

Mass spectrometer. An instrument in which ions are generated and analyzed according to their mass-to-charge ratio, and in which the number of ions is determined electrically.

Mass spectrum. Plot of ion abundance vs. mass-to-charge ratio typically normalized to most abundant ion.

Mass-to-charge ratio (m/z). the dimensionless quantity formed by dividing the mass of an ion in Daltons by the number of charges carried by the ion. For example: for the ion C_7H_7+1, $m/z = 91.0$. For the ion C_7H_7+2, $m/z = 45.5$.

Mass selective detector. A detector that only monitors ion currents at certain m/z values.

Matrix-assisted laser desorption/ionization (MALDI). An ionization source that generates ions by desorbing them from a solid matrix material with a pulsed laser beam.

mDa. MilliDaltons (0.001 Daltons).

mmu. Millimass unit (0.001 Daltons).

Molecular ion. Ion generated from a neutral molecule by the loss or gain of an electron, proton, cation, anion. For example

$M+H)^+$, $(M+Cl)^-$, $(M-H)^-$.

Multiple-charged ions. Ions having more than a single charge.

m/z. An abbreviation used to denote the mass-to-charge-ratio the dimensionless quantity formed by dividing the mass of an ion in Daltons by the number of charges carried by the ion. For example: for the ion $(C_7H_7)^{+1}$, $m/z = 91.0$. For the ion C_7H_7+2, $m/z = 45.5$.

Negative ion. An atom, radical, molecule, or molecular moiety that has gained one of more electrons or lost a positive moiety, thus acquiring an electrically negative charge.

Neutral loss scan. An MS/MS experiment which records all precursor ions which lose a particular neutral fragment.

Nitrogen rule. If a compound contains an even number of nitrogen atoms, its molecular ion will be an even mass number.

Consider compounds containing any or all of the elements C, H, N, and/or O and S. In this case a neutral compound having an even number of nitrogens will have an even number of hydrogens. Conversely, a compound having an odd number of nitrogens will typically have an odd number of hydrogens. Phosphorus will behave as a nitrogen atom such that an even number of nitrogens and one phosphorus will result in an odd number of hydrogens. Halogens can be counted as hydrogens. This

241

rule can be useful when determining the molecular formula of your compound. For a neutral organic compound, elements C, H, N, and/or O and S, an odd number of nitrogens should result in an odd number of hydrogens. And an even number of nitrogens should result in an even number of hydrogens

Examples:

Compound	Formula	Monoisotopic Mass (Da)
Methane	CH_4	14
Methyl Amine	CH_5N	31
Methanol	CH_4O	32
Aniline	C_6H_7N	93
Thioglycerol	$C_3H_8O_2S_1$	108
Peptide (AARNDCCHIIP)	$C_{49}H_{81}N_{17}O_{15}S_2$	1211
Carbohydrate (Lex)	$C_{23}H_{39}N_1O_{15}$	569
Oligonucleotide	$C_{23}H_{38}P_2N_4O_8$	560
Phospholipid	$C_{10}H_{23}P_1O_5$	254

Odd-electron and even-electron ions. Ions can have either an even or odd number of electrons while a neutral, un-ionized compound will have an even number of electrons. Ionization by electron ionization (EI) typically produces a molecular ion that will have an odd number of electrons because one electron is lost during the ionization process. Most fragment ions in EI are formed by the loss of a radical, so most fragment ions have an even-electron configuration. Fragment ions that have an odd-electron configuration are usually the result of a rearrangement process, so it is useful to identify important odd-electron ions in a mass spectrum.

Soft ionization methods such as electrospray ionization, FAB, or CI often produce species such as $[M+H]^+$ or $[M+Na]^+$ that have an even-electron configuration.

The elemental composition calculation includes a parameter that specifies what kinds of elemental compositions are to be included in the analysis report: EVEN-electron ions, ODD-electron ions, or BOTH. This can be used to limit the output. For example, an accurate mass measurement for an $[M+H]^+$ species produced by electrospray ionization or FAB should limit the possible elemental composition to EVEN-electron species. If you are looking for molecular ions in an accurate mass analysis of EI data, limit the output to ODD-electron ions.

Photodissociation. Ion or neutral fragmentation caused by absorption of one or more photons.

Plasma desorption (californium fission fragment desorption). An ionization source that generates ions by desorbing them from a solid matrix material with high-energy fission fragments generated from radioactive californium.

Pneumatically-assisted electrospray. It is achieved by passing a stream of gas (air) over the droplets to facilitate desolvation.

Positive ion. An atom, radical, molecule, or molecular moiety that has lost one or more electrons or gained one or more positive ions, thus acquiring an electrically positive charge.

ppm. parts per million, a term often used in exact mass measurements to describe accuracy. For example, a 2.3 milliDalton (mDa) error for a molecular ion with m/z 545.2034 is equivalent to a relative error of $0.0023 \pm 545 = .0000042$ or 4.2 x 10-6 or 4.2 ppm.

actual =   545.2034

observed =   545.2011 (error = 4.2 ppm)

Resolution (10% valley definition) M/ΔM - Let two peaks of equal height in a mass spectrum at masses m and m-ΔM be separated by a valley that at its lowest point is just 10% of the height of either peak. Then the resolution (10% valley definition) is M/ΔM.

Resolution (peak width definition) M/ΔM - For a single peak made up of singly charged ions of mass m in a mass spectrum, the resolution may be expressed as M/ΔM, where ΔM is the width of the peak at a height that is a specified fraction of the maximum peak height. It is recommended that one of three values 50, 5, or .5% be used. For an isolated symmetrical peak, recorded with a system that is linear in range between 5 and 10% levels of the peak, the 5% peak width definition is technically equivalent to the 10% valley definition. A common standard is the definition of resolution based upon ΔM being the full width of the peak at half its maximum height, sometimes abbreviated "FWHM".

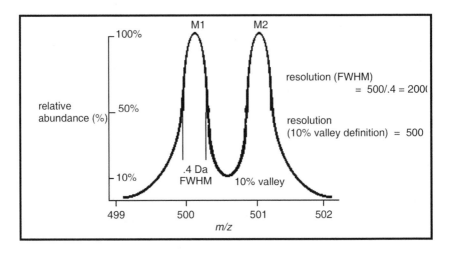

Precursor ion scan. A tandem mass spectrometry experiment which records all precursor ions derived from a single product ion.

Product ion scan. A tandem mass spectrometry experiment which records all product ions derived from a single precursor ion.

Proton affinity. Enthalpy change for the process $MH^+ \quad M + H^+$.

Reflectron. A part of a time-of-flight reflectron mass analyzer that retards and then reverses ion velocities in order to correct for ion flight times for ions having different kinetic energies. The reflectron is sometimes called an ion mirror.

Resolution. Resolving power is the ability of a mass spectrometer to separate two masses (M1, M2) is termed resolution (R). The most common definition of R is $R = M/\Delta M$, in which $\Delta M = M1 - M2$ and $M = M1$. Thus, if a mass spectrometer can separate two masses (100,101), then $\Delta M = 1$, $M = 100$ and $R = 100$. For conventional accurate mass measurements, R needs to be as large as possible. An instrument with R

= 20,000 can separate an ion at 100.0000 from a second mass at 100.0050 ($\Delta M = M/R = 100/20,000 = 0.005$).

To use the formula $R = M/\Delta M$, it is necessary to define at what stage the two peaks representing the two masses are actually separate. The height of the "valley" between the two peaks is used for this prupose, with 5, 10, and 50% valley definitions being in use. A 5% valley definition is a much stricter criterion of separation (resolution) than is the 50% definition.

Secondary ion mass spectrometry. An ionization approach in mass spectrometry that is based on analysis of particles that are emitted when a surface is bombarded by energetic (~keV) primary particles such as Ar^+ and Cs^+.

Selected ion monitoring (SIM). Also known as selected ion recording (SIR). An experiment in which the mass analyzer is used to detect one or a few ions as a function of time. Selecting a particular ion or ions to monitor has the benefit of sensitivity. Since the instrument is not spending time scanning for other ions, it can be dedicated to the ion selected. This can result in large increase in sensitivity, however, the disadvantage is a lack of information. It has been especially useful in biochemistry, medicine, and environmental science where a known compound or compounds required quantification from complex mixtures. SIM with derivatization has also been shown to be very useful with prostaglandins.

Signal-to-noise ratio (SNR). The signal-to-noise ratio is proportional to the square root of the number of samples averaged in scanning the signal. Thus SNR $\alpha \, n1/2$

So, if you average a signal 100 times, the signal-to-noise ratio will increase by a factor of ten.

Tandem mass spectrometry. Coupling two or more mass analyzers or mass analysis events to perform repetitive mass spectrometry experiments. Typically used in conjunction with fragmentation experiments where a particular ion is selected by the first analysis, and then followed by collision-induced dissociation and subsequent analysis of the fragment ions.

Time-of-flight mass spectrometer. A mass analyzer in which ions are accelerated and their flight times measured to determine their mass. Time-of-flight mass spectrometers were originally known as velocitrons.

Total ion current (TIC). The total current generated by all the ions independent of m/z.

Thermospray. An ionization process where a liquid is thermally vaporized and the ions in the resulting aerosol are transferred from the liquid to the gas phase. The ionization process can involve ion evaporation or chemical ionization (the reagent ions are formed by a filament or discharge) ionization of the solvent. Thermospray is not often used any longer because it was superceded by electrospray for applications to biomolecules.

Appendix

Table A.1. Atomic Weights of the Elements Based on the Carbon 12 Standard

Symbol	Mass	Abundance	Symbol	Mass	Abundance	Symbol	Mass	Abundance	Symbol	Mass	Abundance	Symbol	Mass	Abundance
^{1}H	1.0078	99.985	^{53}Cr	52.9407	9.50	^{98}Mo	97.9054	24.13	^{132}Ba	131.9050	0.101	^{175}Lu	174.9408	97.40
^{1}H^{+}	1.0073	99.985	^{54}Cr	53.9389	2.36	^{100}Mo	99.9075	9.63	^{134}Ba	133.9045	2.417	^{176}Lu	175.9427	2.60
^{2}H	2.0141	0.015	^{55}Mn	54.9380	100.00	^{96}Ru	95.9076	5.52	^{135}Ba	134.9057	6.592	^{174}Hf	173.9401	0.16
^{3}He	3.0160	0.00014	^{54}Fe	53.9396	5.80	^{98}Ru	97.9053	1.88	^{136}Ba	135.9046	7.854	^{176}Hf	175.9414	5.20
^{4}He	4.0026	99.99986	^{56}Fe	55.9349	91.72	^{99}Ru	98.9059	12.70	^{137}Ba	136.9058	11.23	^{177}Hf	176.9432	18.60
^{6}Li	6.0151	7.5	^{57}Fe	56.9354	2.20	^{100}Ru	99.9042	12.60	^{138}Ba	137.9052	71.70	^{178}Hf	177.9437	27.10
^{7}Li	7.0160	92.5	^{58}Fe	57.9333	0.28	^{101}Ru	100.9056	17.00	^{138}La	137.9071	0.09	^{179}Hf	178.9458	13.74
^{9}Be	9.0122	100.00	^{59}Co	58.9332	100.00	^{102}Ru	101.9043	31.60	^{139}La	138.9064	99.91	^{180}Hf	179.9466	35.20
^{10}B	10.0129	19.9	^{58}Ni	57.9353	68.27	^{104}Ru	103.9054	18.70	^{136}Ce	135.9071	0.19	^{180}Ta	179.9475	0.012
^{11}B	11.0093	80.1	^{60}Ni	59.9308	26.10	^{103}Rh	102.9055	100.00	^{138}Ce	137.9060	0.25	^{181}Ta	180.9467	99.988
^{12}C	12.0000	98.90	^{61}Ni	60.9311	1.13	^{102}Pd	101.9056	1.02	^{140}Ce	139.9054	88.48	^{180}W	179.9467	0.13
^{13}C	13.0034	1.10	^{62}Ni	61.9283	3.59	^{104}Pd	103.9040	11.14	^{141}Pr	140.9077	100.00	^{182}W	181.9482	26.30
^{14}N	14.0031	99.634	^{64}Ni	63.9280	0.91	^{105}Pd	104.9051	22.33	^{142}Nd	141.9077	27.13	^{183}W	182.9502	14.30
^{15}N	15.0001	0.366	^{63}Cu	62.9296	69.17	^{106}Pd	105.9035	27.33	^{143}Nd	142.9098	12.18	^{184}W	183.9510	30.67
^{16}O	15.9949	99.762	^{65}Cu	64.9278	30.83	^{108}Pd	107.9039	26.46	^{144}Nd	143.9101	23.80	^{186}W	185.9544	23.60
^{17}O	16.9991	0.038	^{64}Zn	63.9291	48.60	^{110}Pd	109.9052	11.72	^{145}Nd	144.9126	8.30	^{30}Si	29.9738	3.10
^{18}O	17.9992	0.200	^{66}Zn	65.9260	27.90	^{107}Ag	106.9051	51.839	^{146}Nd	145.9131	17.19	^{31}P	30.9738	100.00
^{19}F	18.9984	100.00	^{67}Zn	66.9271	4.10	^{109}Ag	108.9048	48.161	^{148}Nd	147.9169	5.76	^{32}S	31.9721	95.02
^{20}Ne	19.9924	90.51	^{68}Zn	67.9248	18.80	^{106}Cd	105.9065	1.25	^{150}Nd	149.9209	5.64	^{33}S	32.9715	0.75
^{21}Ne	20.9938	0.27	^{70}Zn	69.9253	0.60	^{108}Cd	107.9042	0.89	^{144}Sm	143.9120	3.10	^{34}S	33.9679	4.21
^{22}Ne	21.9914	9.22	^{69}Ga	68.9256	60.10	^{110}Cd	109.9030	12.49	^{147}Sm	146.9149	15.00	^{36}S	35.9671	0.02
^{23}Na	22.9898	100.00	^{71}Ga	70.9247	39.90	^{111}Cd	110.9042	12.80	^{148}Sm	147.9148	11.30	^{35}Cl	34.9689	75.77
^{23}Na^{+}	22.9893	100.00	^{70}Ge	69.9242	20.50	^{112}Cd	111.9028	24.13	^{170}Yb	169.9348	3.05	^{37}Cl	36.9660	24.23
^{24}Mg	23.9850	78.99	^{72}Ge	71.9221	27.40	^{113}Cd	112.9044	12.22	^{171}Yb	170.9363	14.30	^{36}Ar	35.9675	0.337
^{25}Mg	24.9858	10.00	^{73}Ge	72.9235	7.80	^{114}Cd	113.9034	28.73	^{172}Yb	171.9364	21.90	^{38}Ar	37.9627	0.063
^{26}Mg	25.9826	11.01	^{74}Ge	73.9212	36.50	^{134}Xe	133.9054	10.40	^{173}Yb	172.9382	16.12	^{40}Ar	39.9624	99.600
^{27}Al	26.9815	100.00	^{76}Ge	75.9214	7.80	^{136}Xe	135.9072	8.90	^{174}Yb	173.9389	31.80	^{39}K	38.9626	93.2581
^{28}Si	27.9769	92.23	^{96}Mo	95.9047	16.68	^{133}Cs	132.9054	100.00				^{40}K	39.9637	0.0117

Symbol	Mass	Abundance
^{29}Si	28.9765	4.67
^{40}Ca	39.9626	96.941
^{42}Ca	41.9586	0.647
^{43}Ca	42.9588	0.135
^{44}Ca	43.9555	2.086
^{46}Ca	45.9537	0.004
^{48}Ca	47.9525	0.187
^{45}**Sc**	44.9559	100.00
^{46}**Ti**	45.9526	8.0
^{47}Ti	46.9518	7.3
^{48}Ti	47.9479	73.8
^{49}Ti	48.9479	5.5
^{50}Ti	49.9448	5.4
^{50}V	49.9472	0.250
^{51}V	50.9440	99.750
^{50}Cr	49.9460	4.35
^{52}Cr	51.9405	83.79
^{75}**As**	74.9216	100.00
^{74}Se	73.9225	0.90
^{76}Se	75.9192	9.00
^{77}Se	76.9199	7.60
^{78}Se	77.9173	23.50
^{80}Se	79.9165	49.60
^{82}Se	81.9167	9.40
^{79}Br	78.9183	50.69
^{81}**Br**	80.9163	49.31
^{78}**Kr**	77.9204	0.35
^{80}Kr	79.9164	2.25
^{82}Kr	81.9135	11.60
^{83}Kr	82.9141	11.50
^{84}Kr	83.9115	57.00
^{97}Mo	96.9060	9.55
^{86}Kr	85.9106	17.30
^{85}**Rb**	84.9118	72.165
^{87}Rb	86.9092	27.835
^{84}Sr	83.9134	0.56
^{86}Sr	85.9093	9.86
^{87}Sr	86.9089	7.00
^{88}Sr	87.9056	82.58
^{89}Y	88.9059	100.00
^{90}Zr	89.9047	51.45
^{91}Zr	90.9050	11.27
^{92}Zr	91.9050	17.17
^{94}Zr	93.9063	17.33
^{96}Zr	95.9083	02.78
^{93}**Nb**	92.9064	100.00
^{92}**Mo**	91.9068	14.84
^{94}Mo	93.9051	9.25
^{95}Mo	94.9058	15.92
^{116}**Cd**	115.9048	7.49
^{113}**In**	112.9041	4.30
^{115}In	114.9039	95.70
^{112}**Sn**	111.9048	1.00
^{114}Sn	113.9028	0.70
^{115}Sn	114.9033	0.40
^{116}Sn	115.9017	14.70
^{117}Sn	116.9030	7.70
^{118}Sn	117.9016	24.30
^{119}Sn	118.9033	08.60
^{120}Sn	119.9022	32.40
^{122}Sn	121.9034	4.60
^{124}Sn	123.9053	5.60
^{130}**Ba**	129.9063	0.106
^{121}**Sb**	120.9038	57.30
^{123}Sb	122.9042	42.70
^{120}**Te**	119.9040	0.096
^{122}Te	121.9031	2.60
^{123}Te	122.9043	0.908
^{124}Te	123.9028	4.816
^{125}Te	124.9044	7.14
^{126}Te	125.9033	18.95
^{128}Te	127.9045	31.69
^{130}Te	129.9062	33.80
^{127}I	126.9045	100.00
^{124}**Xe**	123.9061	0.10
^{126}Xe	125.9043	0.09
^{128}Xe	127.9035	1.91
^{129}Xe	128.9048	26.40
^{130}Xe	129.9035	4.10
^{131}Xe	130.9051	21.20
^{132}Xe	131.9041	26.90
^{149}Sm	148.9172	13.80
^{150}Sm	149.9173	7.40
^{152}Sm	151.9197	26.70
^{154}Sm	153.9209	22.70
^{151}**Eu**	150.9199	47.80
^{153}Eu	152.9212	52.20
^{152}**Gd**	151.9198	0.20
^{154}Gd	153.9209	2.18
^{155}Gd	154.9226	14.80
^{156}Gd	155.9221	20.47
^{157}Gd	156.9240	15.65
^{158}Gd	157.9241	24.84
^{176}Yb	175.9426	12.70
^{160}Gd	159.9271	21.86
^{159}**Tb**	158.9254	100.00
^{156}**Dy**	155.9243	0.06
^{158}Dy	157.9244	0.10
^{160}Dy	159.9252	2.34
^{161}Dy	160.9269	18.90
^{162}Dy	161.9268	25.50
^{163}Dy	162.9287	24.90
^{164}Dy	163.9292	28.20
^{165}**Ho**	164.9303	100.00
^{162}**Er**	161.9288	0.14
^{164}Er	163.9292	1.61
^{166}Er	165.9303	33.60
^{167}Er	166.9321	22.95
^{168}Er	167.9324	26.80
^{170}Er	169.9355	14.90
^{169}**Tm**	168.9342	100.00
^{168}Yb	167.9339	0.13
^{189}**Os**	188.9582	16.10
^{190}Os	189.9585	26.40
^{192}Os	191.9615	41.00
^{191}**Ir**	190.9606	37.30
^{193}Ir	192.9629	62.70
^{190}Pt	189.9599	0.01
^{192}Pt	191.9610	0.79
^{194}Pt	193.9627	32.90
^{195}Pt	194.9648	32.80
^{196}Pt	195.9649	25.30
^{198}Pt	197.9679	7.20
^{197}**Au**	196.9666	100.00
^{41}K	40.9618	6.7302
^{196}**Hg**	195.9658	0.15
^{198}Hg	197.9668	10.10
^{199}Hg	198.9683	17.00
^{200}Hg	199.9683	23.10
^{201}Hg	200.9703	13.20
^{202}Hg	201.9706	29.65
^{204}Hg	203.9735	6.80
^{203}Tl	202.9723	29.524
^{205}Tl	203.9744	70.476
^{204}**Pb**	203.9730	1.40
^{206}Pb	205.9745	24.10
^{207}Pb	206.9759	22.10
^{208}Pb	207.9766	52.40
^{209}**Bi**	208.9804	100.00
^{232}**Th**	232.0381	100.00
^{234}U	234.0409	0.0055
^{235}U	235.0439	0.7200
^{238}U	238.0508	99.2745

Table A.2.
Amino acids and their mass organized in alphabetical order.

Amino Acid	Letter Code		Mass	R
(Alphabetical Order)				
Alanine	Ala	A	71	-CH3
Arginine	Arg	R	156	-CH2(CH2)2NH-C=NHNH2
Aspargine	Asn	N	114	-CH2CONH2
Aspartic Acid	Asp	D	115	-CH2COOH
Cysteine	Cys	C	103	-CH2SH
Glutamic Acid	Glu	E	129	-CH2CH2COOH
Glutamine	Gln	Q	128	-CH2CH2CONH2
Glycine	Gly	G	57	-H
Histidine	His	H	137	-CH2 (imidazole ring)
Isoleucine	Ile	I	113	-CH(CH3)CH2CH3
Leucine	Leu	L	113	-CH2CH(CH3)2
Lysine	Lys	K	128	-CH2(CH2)3NH2
Methionine	Met	M	131	-CH2CH2SCH3
Phenylalanine	Phe	F	147	-CH2-phenyl
Proline	Pro	P	97	(pyrrolidine ring structure)
Serine	Ser	S	87	-CH2OH
Threonine	Thr	T	101	-CH(OH)CH3
Tryptophan	Trp	W	186	-CH2 (indole ring)
Tyrosine	Tyr	Y	163	-CH2-*para*-phenol
Valine	Val	V	99	-CH(CH3)2

Table A.3.
Amino acids and their mass organized in according to molecular weight order.

$$-N-\underset{\underset{H}{|}}{\overset{\overset{R}{|}}{C}}-\overset{\overset{O}{\|}}{C}-$$
(H H)

Amino Acid	Letter Code		Mass	R
(By Mass)				
Glycine	Gly	G	57	-H
Alanine	Ala	A	71	-CH3
Serine	Ser	S	87	-CH2OH
Proline	Pro	P	97	(pyrrolidine ring structure)
Valine	Val	V	99	-CH(CH3)2
Threonine	Thr	T	101	-CH(OH)CH3
Cysteine	Cys	C	103	-CH2SH
Isoleucine	Ile	I	113	-CH(CH3)CH2CH3
Leucine	Leu	L	113	-CH2CH(CH3)2
Aspargine	Asn	N	114	-CH2CONH2
Aspartic Acid	Asp	D	115	-CH2COOH
Glutamine	Gln	Q	128	-CH2CH2CONH2
Lysine	Lys	K	128	-CH2(CH2)3NH2
Glutamic Acid	Glu	E	129	-CH2CH2COOH
Methionine	Met	M	131	-CH2CH2SCH3
Histidine	His	H	137	-CH2 (imidazole ring structure)
Phenylalanine	Phe	F	147	-CH2-phenyl
Arginine	Arg	R	156	-CH2(CH2)2NH-C=NHNH2
Tyrosine	Tyr	Y	163	-CH2-*para*-phenol
Tryptophan	Trp	W	186	-CH2 (indole ring structure)

251

Index

Author Note

Gary Siuzdak obtained his Ph.D. at Darthmouth College and is currently at The Scripps Research Institute where he is Director of the Center for Mass Spectrometry and Associate Professor of Molecular Biology. And learned to ride the bicycle at 3.